A Black Bear's Story

Also by Emil E. Liers

AN OTTER'S STORY

A BEAVER'S STORY

A BLACK BEAR'S STORY

by *Emil E. Liers*

ILLUSTRATED BY RAY SHERIN

THE VIKING PRESS

New York

First published in 1962 by The Viking Press, Inc.
625 Madison Avenue, New York 22, N. Y.

Published simultaneously in Canada
by The Macmillan Company of Canada Limited

Library of Congress catalog card number: 62-9629

SECOND PRINTING SEPTEMBER 1964

PRINTED IN THE U. S. A. BY MURRAY PRINTING CO.

To the American Black Bear

May man's expanding civilization never wholly crowd this native American from his natural haunts.

May we always preserve our wilderness and deep woods, sheltering the black bear and all his wildlife neighbors. The fun-loving cubs, the patient and devoted mothers, the black bear males who roam the forests like majestic shadows—these are part of our American heritage.

May they always live wild and free in our American wilderness, sharing with man the peace and beauty of our deep forests, lakes, and streams.

Contents

8   *Contents*

A Black Bear's Story

1. Winter Wilderness

In the wilderness area of far northern Minnesota a full moon was setting in the northwest skies. It was a cold, still, clear morning at the end of January. The sky was still dark as the great white-gold moon sank toward the spruce tops, and now and then the quiet air resounded with the cracks of freezing trees. At times the ground itself quivered, blanketed deep with snow, as an extra loud report told of the frost that was causing the trees and the earth to contract in the sub-zero cold.

Soon the moon, in flaming yellow, disappeared behind a hilltop. Light began to creep across the southeastern sky. Steadily the sky brightened until the sun, flaming still more brightly, rose above the horizon. This was the time of day when the temperature reached its lowest point. As brilliant sunlight crept through the treetops, the leafless birches and aspens shivered in the intense cold, and it seemed that no creature could be alive in all these silent, snow-covered woods.

As the sun rose higher in the sky, its rays penetrated deep into a cedar swamp in the Sawtooth Mountains north of Lake Superior's northwest shore. Years ago these Minnesota hills had been a towering mountain range. Many years of wind and ice and rain had worn them away until they were left as the present granite hills, surrounded by a forest wilderness of spruce and pine, birch and aspen.

In a low spot among these hills, southeast of Brule Lake and near the headwaters of the Cascade River, the cedar swamp lay snowbound below a long pine-covered ridge. Great old cedar trees lay uprooted among the dense and tangled growth of young cedars and black spruces. Alder brush and red-osier dogwood grew in the small boggy clearings. Ice locked the marshy bottoms of the swamp, but here and there a trickling spring still welled up, unfrozen, from deep below the surface. In the early-morning sunlight there was no sound, no movement, no sign of life, save for the hushed murmur of the springs.

Suddenly a raven's croaking call came from nowhere. For several minutes the caller remained hidden. Then he came gliding on wide black wings from one pine top to another, throwing his voice like a ventriloquist. Now came the tap, tap, tap of an Arctic three-toed woodpecker, searching the tree trunks for his breakfast. As sunlight flooded the forest, nuthatches and chickadees emerged from their hollow-tree sleeping quarters, and soon their cheerful voices and lilting flight filled the wintry woods with life and gaiety.

The tiny hearts of these small birds pump blood very rapidly through their bodies, and their loose feather coverings also help to keep them warm. But in the frigid winter months they must search for food constantly in order to sustain life. Even in the snowy north woods Nature usually provides plenty for the birds to eat, but they must keep active to find these hidden tidbits. All winter long the chickadees and nuthatches keep busy flitting from tree to bush, searching for seeds and pine cones or for hibernating insects and caterpillars.

In the cedar swamp a red-breasted nuthatch crept head first down a spruce trunk, calling his nasal "yank, yank" to his mate. A black-capped chickadee flew down to where a giant cedar lay uprooted in the swamp. Searching systematically in the loose bark for a beetle or grub, she soon reached the up-turned roots of the cedar. Just ready to fly on to another tree, the chickadee stopped for a moment, attracted by strange murmuring sounds that came from a rough, cavelike opening under the roots.

The listening bird cocked her head curiously, first to one side and then to the other, her sparkling black eyes trying to find the source of these strange sounds. Flitting beneath the great mass of snow-covered roots, she peered through a tangle of brush and cedar branches into a dark hollow below the dead cedar trunk. As the chickadee's eyes became accustomed to the half-light, she saw at last where the strange sounds came from. Deep in the dusky hollow, two little bear cubs

were crooning softly as they nursed between the arms of a large black mother bear.

When the old cedar crashed to earth the summer before, it bent the branches of several young cedars and other bushes beneath its weight. These branches formed a canopy beneath the slanting fallen trunk, and with the mass of roots above and the earth hollow below, the mother black bear had made a cozy nest in which to spend the winter.

One week ago, late in January, the mother bear had given birth to two babies. It was their nursing song that the chicka-dee had heard, a happy purring lullaby that they crooned as they sucked their mother's good warm milk. The drowsy mother bear cuddled the cubs against her furry body and watched the chickadee without alarm. She knew the inquisitive bird at the entrance to her den meant no harm. Soon, when the babies' stomachs were full, mother and cubs all drifted off to sleep together in their dark, protected nest. Out in the cold winter sunshine the chickadee went on her way, searching for breakfast and chattering merrily about the new life in the frozen north woods.

2. Kabato and Her Babies

The mother black bear was called Kabato, which means "runner" in the Chippewa tongue. She was not unusually large for a black bear, weighing about three hundred pounds, but she could run with great speed if the need arose. In spite of her thickset body, stocky legs, and large clawed feet, she could move along the forest trails as swiftly and silently as a shadow.

Kabato's coat was of thick and glossy fur, about four inches long in the wintertime. Unlike some black bears, she had true jet-black fur, with just one large white spot on her chest. In spite of their name, black bears may have fur in a whole range of colors from black to brown to reddish or yellowish tan. Kabato's face and nose were tinged with tan where the black fur ended, and her bright black eyes were set close together across a straight muzzle. Her eyesight was not as good as a bobcat's or a man's, but her round furry ears caught every sound, and her keen sense of smell told her all the secrets of the woods.

Kabato had lived all her life in the Superior National Forest of northern Minnesota. She was born a few miles north of Grand Marais, near the rocky shore of Lake Superior. All during her six years of life she had roamed that wild north country, exploring the many rockbound lakes and dense pine forests, the granite ridges and open muskeg marshes, the brushy hillsides, the many ice-cold streams that rushed and plunged down rapids and waterfalls, down from the ancient Sawtooth Mountains into the vast blue expanse of Lake Superior, the "shining big-sea water" of the Indians.

In her six years Kabato had learned much black-bear wisdom. She had learned where to find food of many kinds in this northern wilderness; who her enemies were among the other creatures, and who were her friends; when to begin preparations for the long winter sleep, and how to find a den sheltered from the snow and icy winds.

Three years ago Kabato had found a mate. In her eyes he was the finest black bear in all the northern woods, a large brown-headed male called Koda—"friend" in Chippewa—a power in the forest, yet always gentle with Kabato. According to black-bear ways, they traveled and lived together only in mating season; but he was Kabato's mate for life, no matter how far apart their paths in the wilderness might sometimes take them. Kabato's first cub, born two years ago, had been killed while still a baby by cruel hunters, and ever since she had dimly felt a loss and a longing that only her new cubs could ease.

Late the summer before, and all through the fall, Kabato had eaten heartily, storing up a thick layer of fat under her fur so that she could go without food and keep warm during the winter months. In November, when she was plump and sleek with her fur grown long, she made her nest under the fallen cedar in the swamp. There she drowsed the months away, neither eating nor drinking, but sleeping most of the time.

Like all bears, Kabato was not a true hibernator as are woodchucks, gophers, and chipmunks, whose body temperatures drop to near the air temperature in their winter nests, and whose heartbeat and other body processes are greatly slowed. Although bears have a lower respiration rate during their winter sleep, breathing only three or four times a minute, their body temperature remains nearly normal, and they are awake for part of the time.

Late in January, Kabato's two cubs were born, and now they cuddled, just one week old, in the arms of their proud but sleepy mother. The newborn babies, one a male and one a female, were homely little creatures by human standards, just as newborn human babies often are. But to Kabato they were dear and beautiful.

Their bodies, about ten inches long, were covered with black hair so thin and fine they looked almost naked. Each weighed about eight ounces when it was born, only one-six-hundredth as much as their three-hundred-pound mother. They were no bigger than otter babies, although a mother otter might weigh only twenty pounds! Beaver and porcupine babies are twice as big as baby bears at birth, though a mother beaver usually weighs only thirty pounds and a porcupine only fifteen. Why do black bears have such tiny babies? That is one of Nature's riddles that no one has yet answered.

The baby bears were born with their eyes tight closed, like kittens. They had little bobbed tails but big feet with short, curving claws. These large flat feet seemed ungainly and out of proportion to the rest of their bodies now, but as the cubs grew older their powerful feet would be very important to them. The broad soles would enable them to walk softly through the forests or scoop fish from a stream, and the short, sturdy claws would help them to climb trees easily and tear apart logs and stumps to find food.

As the winter days went by, the twin cubs did little but eat and sleep in their nest in the cedar swamp. Kabato held them close as they suckled and crooned, and soon she drifted off to sleep herself. Sometimes one baby would roll away from Kabato's big warm body into a draft of cold air or a small drift of snow near the den entrance. It would whimper and cry as the cold struck its thin-haired body. Then Kabato would nuzzle the little lost cub and help it back to the shelter of her thick, warm fur.

By the third week both cubs showed their adventurous spirit by sometimes wandering away from Kabato's side on purpose, even though their eyes were still closed. They would wobble blindly a few feet deeper into the den, or crawl in exploration over their sleepy mother's big body. When they came to a rounded, steep place on her back or haunches, where they could not cling, down and away they would roll, out to the cold edges of the hollow.

Whenever the wind blew and snow sifted in through the den entrance, Kabato turned her broad back to the opening and shielded the cubs from the cold and snow. One would think that Kabato could have made a warmer, tighter den for their winter quarters. But bears are sturdy creatures and do not

mind a little snow. With four inches of thick fur and a four-inch layer of fat below that, a bear past cubhood manages to keep warm in almost any winter shelter. Sometimes in late fall a black bear may get sleepy before he finds a den. Then he curls up right in the open and drowses away the winter with only a deep snow blanket for protection. Kabato knew that her den, even though drafty, was safe and warm enough for her babies.

In their first week of life the cubs doubled in size and weight. Week after week they grew bigger and stronger on their diet of warm bear milk. Cuddling close to Kabato, right under her arms, they had four nipples on which to nurse, or for variety they could suck on two more just ahead of her hind legs.

The floor of the den, lined with the grass and leaves and pine needles that Kabato had gathered last November, stayed clean and fresh week after week, with no odor or waste material apparent from either the mother bear or her cubs. How this can be explained, no one can say for certain. Perhaps Kabato kept her babies and nest licked clean as mother otters, dogs, and cats do. Or it may be that while the mother bear is in her winter den the cubs digest all their milk with no residue. Whatever the explanation, after the three months or more that the cubs spend nursing and growing in the den, the nest is still sweet-smelling and clean when the family leaves in April or May. Here is another of Nature's marvelous riddles that help to guard and protect her children.

3. Anang and Anoki

As the two little bear cubs grew larger and stronger, they became more active. Even before their eyes were open they spent much time in play, wrestling and boxing with each other and climbing all over Kabato as she slept. If in their exciting games they tumbled out of bounds into the cold, they whimpered and cried like human babies. Kabato would wake from her slumber and, with a soft grunt to the blind cubs, call them back to her sheltering arms.

When the cubs were thirty-five days old their eyes were ready to open. As they looked about their home in the dim half-light it seemed vast and mysterious to them, with its dark recesses under the slanting cedar trunk and the tangle of small trees and brush bent over under the cedar's weight. Now that they could see, it was harder than ever for them to stay put. They wanted to explore every part of their home under the brush and snow.

They wanted to investigate Kabato too, now that they could see what this big, kind, furry mother who kept them so warm and full of milk looked like. They crawled all over her, pulling at her lips and ears and tugging at her short fur-covered tail. When they tugged too hard, Kabato growled a deep, rumbling growl. But the babies knew it was not as serious as it sounded.

At six weeks the cubs were already developing their own individual personalities. The little male cub was called Anang, the Chippewa word for "star," because of the white star-shaped mark on his chest. He was adventurous and inquisitive like his sister, but he was more cautious than she and not such a daredevil in their romps about the den. Anang was good-natured and affectionate with his sister, and even when they squabbled and cuffed each other, he was careful never really to hurt her.

Anoki, his sister, was a saucy little minx, a little smaller than Anang but quicker and surer-footed. She always wanted to climb higher and somersault more daringly than her brother. She was more agile than Anang and loved to tease him and show off her skill at climbing. Her name, Anoki, was the Chippewa word for "actor," and it suited this little show-off very well.

One day late in February, even before the cubs' eyes were open, Anoki had sniffed her inquisitive way to the back of the cave where the bent trunks of some alder bushes came out of the ground. Experimentally Anoki stood up on her hind legs and grasped a small alder trunk with her forepaws. It felt firm and secure, and in a moment she was pulling herself up the slanting alder bole, gripping tight with her short, curved claws. She was about three feet up in the air on her first tree-climbing expedition when she lost her balance and began to fall.

Anoki dug in with all her claws and hung on, swinging upside down below the slanting alder and crying in fright. Without sight she could not tell how high she was, and now the little daredevil didn't feel nearly so bold. Anoki's piteous cry woke up Kabato. She sat up quickly to see what was wrong. But when she saw Anoki only three feet from the ground, she knew there was no danger to her youngster. Bear cubs can and do fall far greater distances without harm, and Kabato decided it was time Anoki learned that. With a reassuring grunt she turned her back and ignored Anoki's wailings.

Hearing her mother's grunt, Anoki lost some of her terror, but she whimpered and whined a while longer, expecting to be rescued. Soon, however, she discovered that swinging below the alder branch was fun, and she rocked and swung delightedly, calling for Anang to come and see how clever she was. But Anang was asleep, curled up beside Kabato. When Anoki tired of her game, she found her arms were strong enough to pull herself back up on top of the branch and scramble backward down to the ground. Thus she postponed her first lesson in falling out of trees, and soon she was sound asleep, exhausted, snuggled next to her mother and brother.

When the cubs' eyes were open, Anoki and Anang were more eager than ever to explore the back reaches of the den and the tangle of brush and branches beyond. Anoki soon found the alder branch she had swung on and proudly showed Anang how it was done. Soon they were both climbing the small alder tree, shinning up the trunk and swinging in unison from the slanting bough.

Anang was the one who discovered that falling was the quickest and easiest way to get down. When he tired of swinging he simply let go the branch, and plump! he tumbled in a soft round ball to the floor of the den. He was so relaxed it didn't hurt a bit, and he was delighted with his new accomplishment. Now he had a trick to show off to Anoki, and he couldn't help lording it over her a bit.

Before long Anoki had learned the trick of falling too. This was as much fun as climbing and swinging. Squealing happily, they scrambled up the branches and tumbled down, over and over, rolling and wrestling and somersaulting in between. Sometimes they scrambled back to where Kabato was trying to sleep, climbed up in the mass of cedar roots above her, and dropped down on her big furry body. She made a wonderful soft mattress to bounce on, but poor Mama Kabato got little sleep with all this squalling and bouncing about. The cubs were full of energy from drinking Kabato's nourishing milk, but Kabato herself had had nothing to eat and needed to rest a great deal to sustain her own strength and provide the cubs with milk.

One day early in March the cubs ventured outside the den for the first time in their lives. It was a mild, sunny day with the temperature just below freezing. There was a moist, fresh smell in the air that seemed to promise spring was not too far away. The fresh air and the brightness of the sun and snow outside tempted Anang and Anoki to explore the strange bright world beyond the entrance to their den.

Cautiously the cubs climbed over Kabato's sleeping body that guarded the entrance. If she awoke, she might forbid their adventure; so today, for once, Anang and Anoki tried very hard not to disturb their mother's slumber. At the entrance two little black noses poked out from under the protective brush and roots, sniffing eagerly at the exciting world outside.

Anoki, as usual the bolder one, was first to scramble out from beneath the cedar roots. Anang came close behind her, and together they gazed in wonder about the vast tangle of the cedar swamp.

Overhead patches of bright blue sky stretched between the dark green spruce and cedar boughs. Fallen tree trunks and bare alder branches made dark patterns against the thick

covering of snow, and the snow itself was criss-crossed with trails made by the deer and snowshoe rabbits. Anang and Anoki floundered awkwardly in the deep snow, not knowing what to think of this white furry stuff that was so cold and soft and gave way so unexpectedly under their feet.

Anang soon pulled himself up onto the fallen cedar tree that formed the roof of their den. Here he could grip the slanting trunk with his claws and he felt more secure. Calling happily to Anoki, he began to climb the cedar trunk. Anoki followed, not to be outdone, and before long they had both reached the cedar top, which now lay some ten or twelve feet above the ground. That was no distance at all to daredevil Anoki. Down she dropped into a snowdrift, and back she plowed through the snow to the base of the cedar to start the climb all over again. Anang came tumbling after her, and soon they had worn a trail of their own beside the fallen cedar, playing their new tree-climbing game.

As twilight darkened the sky, a stern and anxious grunt from Kabato called the tired adventurers back to the safety of the den. Kabato gave each cub a mild but effective cuff of her paw as they crept in. The mother bear knew that her cubs must learn by doing and needed to explore the world outside; but she knew too that they must obey their mother without question and respect her discipline. Many times in the future—and much sooner than they knew—the cubs' very lives would depend on their prompt obedience of Kabato's orders. Chastened but wiser, the two little bears snuggled back into their mother's arms for their evening meal and the long night's rest.

4. High Water—and Wolves

In mid-March there was an early spring thaw. First came two days of clear, sunshiny weather with a warm south wind. The drifts of snow shrank and became wet and soggy where the sun struck deep into the cedar swamp. Patches of bare, damp earth appeared in the deer and rabbit trails where the snow was worn thin. Then the sky clouded over. The cloud cover held the warm air stationary over northern Minnesota, and before long rain began to fall, the first rain since late last October. The rain fell all one night and the next day, melting the snow and filling the cedar swamp with pools and streams of water. Water ran everywhere. It could not sink downward into the still frozen earth, so it rose and spread into every nook and hollow.

In Kabato's den beneath the fallen cedar the water rose steadily. At first Kabato and the cubs were able to keep dry and warm by moving back from the entrance of the den onto a higher ledge at the rear. But the trickling water kept rising, and soon there was no dry spot in the den. With wet paws and fur, the cold and miserable cubs whimpered and clung close to Kabato, trying to find warmth and comfort next to her protective body.

But even Kabato's fur was wet and chilly now. She herself was warm, but with wet fur she could not warm the cubs. Drowsy though she was, she knew they must leave the den at once and find new quarters where her babies would be warm and dry. At the den entrance she sniffed anxiously at the damp air, wondering where to find a safe new home for Anang and Anoki. As she caught the scent of pine from the ridge above the swamp, she remembered an overhanging cliff at the far end of the ridge where she had slept one night last fall. She would try to take her cubs there and find shelter.

Kabato grunted to Anang and Anoki, calling them to follow her. Then she struck out slowly across the flooded cedar swamp. The cubs were more than seven weeks old now, weighing about three pounds apiece. Though they were still only babies, their playful tumbling and climbing about the den had helped to develop and strengthen their muscles, so that they were strong enough to scramble along after their mother. On solid ground and climbing over fallen trees they made good progress under Kabato's watchful eye. But when they came to deeper water, in the flooded parts of the swamp, Kabato picked up each cub in turn and, walking on her hind legs, carried it in her arms and mouth to higher ground.

The rain fell steadily as they made their way through the wild tangle of the swamp and up the side of the pine-covered ridge. When they finally reached level ground at the top, Kabato knew that not many hours of daylight remained. She must find shelter for the cubs soon, since nightfall might bring much colder temperatures.

As Anang and Anoki rested at the top of the ridge, Kabato tried to warm the tired and whimpering cubs. She cradled them close to her body, licking their fuzzy wet fur in an attempt to dry them. Suddenly she heard a sound that raised the hair along her neck and back and drove all lingering drowsiness from her brain. From down the ridge came the long howl of a timber wolf. "Ah-ooooo-ooo" came the wolf call from the distant pines, and "Ah-ooo-ooo-ooo" came an answering howl not more than a hundred yards from the big white pine beneath which Kabato and the cubs were resting.

In a flash Kabato was on her feet. She gave two urgent low-pitched grunts, "Koff, koff"—her warning signal, meaning "Danger!"—and boosted the cubs quickly up the trunk of the big pine. Anang and Anoki needed no further urging. They clambered up the rough trunk as fast as their tired legs and sharp claws would take them. All their play at climbing in and around the den stood them in good stead, and they climbed their first big tree as if they had always known how. They didn't stop till they reached two big branches about twenty feet up. There they clung, one on each side of the trunk, cold and

frightened but safe for the moment and sheltered by the spreading branches from the driving rain.

Below, Kabato turned fiercely to face the threatening wolves. First one, then another and another silently emerged, like shadows, from among the pines. There were seven wolves in the pack, all members of one family. The biggest were as big as huge dogs, with shaggy gray fur and massive heads and jaws. The wolf pack had been cruising along the ridge most of the day, catching and eating mice, shrews, and voles that

were driven to high ground by the rise of water in the swamp. When they scented the bears, they approached with caution. They knew a mother bear could be a terrible adversary, but they were eager to add the baby bears to their menu.

Warily the wolves circled Kabato and the tree where the cubs were clinging. Swift as lightning, Kabato charged each wolf as it approached, gathering all the strength in her powerfully built body. At each charge the wolves scattered and ran in different directions, keeping out of reach of her dangerous

claws and teeth. Then they would circle back, surrounding Kabato and the cubs' pine tree once more. Time after time Kabato charged, enraged and desperate at this threat to her babies. But the crafty wolves did not let her get near them, for they feared the great strength of her forearms and sharp, slashing claws.

It was an unequal battle, with seven well-fed wolves pitted against one fasting mother bear; but Kabato fought fiercely, despite her growing weariness. The rain still descended in torrents, but the wind was changing now to the northwest and cold flakes of snow were interspersed among the raindrops. High in the pine tree, Anang and Anoki began to shiver and cry, not knowing whether they were more cold or more afraid of the wolves below.

As the bear cubs clung and cried in the pine branches, several ravens soared into another pine nearby to find out what the excitement was all about. The great black birds were hungry, and they hoped to share in the wolves' kill. With their sharp, heavy bills they could peck at the eyes of the helpless baby bears, killing them or knocking them down to the ground where the wolves could get at them.

Never in their short lives had Anang and Anoki been in such great peril. In a few weeks they would be big and strong enough to defend themselves against such enemies, but now they could only cling to their branches and cry. Kabato would defend them from the wolves below, but who would protect them from the greedy ravens?

5. A Battle on the Ridge

The answer came from an unexpected quarter. A short distance up the ridge stood a giant old white pine, hollow at the bottom and top, but living still, with sound wood in between. In the hollow stub at the top of the tree a great horned owl had laid her eggs in February, and now she had two owlets in her nest.

Bubo, the father owl, was roosting nearby in the lower branches of a dense spruce thicket. He had hunted in the rain all the previous night, finding mice and shrews to feed his mate and babies. Now he was tired and wanted to sleep, but the howling of the wolves, the crying of the bear cubs, and the excited croaking of the ravens disturbed him. He was alarmed by all this commotion so close to his family's nest. In anger the owl flew to the pine where the ravens were gathering closer and closer about Anang and Anoki.

One raven, bigger than all the rest, was sidling along the branch to which Anoki clung, whining in fright. The raven was almost close enough to give poor Anoki a hard peck with his beak, when suddenly a great gray form with widespread wings swooped toward them. With talons outstretched, the owl sailed straight into the offending raven and knocked him senseless. The stunned raven fell heavily to the ground, black feathers floating after him. Before he regained consciousness, a wolf had got him.

As the great horned owl wheeled to attack the other ravens, they all flew up, croaking their war cry against the enemy. On wide silent wings Bubo flew away from the giant pine where his family nested, far away from the ridge and the cedar swamp, with all the angry ravens giving chase. He led them miles away from the owlets and the baby bears, and only when he felt sure the ravens would not return to the ridge did he drop down into the forest to hide in a balsam thicket.

While the owl lured the ravens away, Anoki clung to her branch in the pine tree, crying piteously. She was so cold and tired she hardly realized she had been saved from a great danger, the ravens' beaks, or that her mother was still fighting below to save them from an even greater danger. Anang had stopped whimpering, using all his strength to cling tightly to the pine trunk and the sheltering branches; but he too was shivering and exhausted.

Beneath the pine tree the melting snow was trampled and

bloodstained with the marks of battle. One of Kabato's hind legs was bleeding where a wolf had bitten her, and several of the wolves bore wounds from the mother bear's slashing claws. But the wolves would not give up. Round and round they circled Kabato, just out of reach. As one wolf challenged her head-on, another ran up to bite her from behind. In rage and pain Kabato wheeled and charged, moving as swiftly as her name, "the runner," promised. More than once she raked her tormentors with her claws; but there were seven of them to her one, and another wolf was always waiting to attack again.

For nearly an hour now the wolf pack had harried Kabato. They nipped and parried, advanced and retreated, until Kabato, crazed with anger and worry for her cubs, was near exhaustion. Time after time she tried to lead the pack away from the pine tree where the cubs were clinging, but one wolf always stayed by the tree, hungrily watching and hoping for the cubs to fall.

Dusk began to darken the sky and the wind grew colder still, swirling the snowflakes that now had replaced the rain entirely. Suddenly, above the moan of the wind in the pine boughs and the swish of falling snow, there came a new sound along the ridge—the muffled thunder of many hoofs. Out of the shadowy twilight a herd of more than twenty deer burst into view at full gallop. They ran in long, graceful leaps, their white tails held high in alarm and their sharp hoofs pounding through the new snow.

Like all the other creatures in the cedar swamp, the deer had been forced from their winter yard by high water. Travel-

ing to a new resting place, they had been frightened by the cry
of a bobcat behind them on the ridge trail, and now, running
in terror, one behind another, at high speed, they burst without
warning upon Kabato and the circling wolves.

There was no time for the deer to retreat, no trail to follow
but the narrow path along the ridge toward the river. In panic
the deer rushed onward, bowling over the startled wolves and
sending them head over heels with their flying hoofs. The herd
raced by like an express train, leaving the wolves so scattered
and confused that it took them several moments to realize
what had happened.

Deer, not bear cubs, were the wolves' natural prey in the wilderness; and as the scent of the herd filled the air and the pounding of its hoofs echoed in the dusk, the father and leader of the wolf pack leaped to the chase. With an excited howl he called his family to follow. In an instant the whole pack was racing down the ridge in full cry after the deer, the mother bear and her cubs forgotten in the thought of such tender meat as the deer herd might provide.

The deer had a flying start, and the wolves were soon outdistanced. On solid ground and for moderate distances, deer can outrun wolves. But in deep snow deer lose their advantage, and their endurance and stamina cannot equal their enemies'. The wolves kept to the trail, yapping in excitement and spurring the frightened deer to run even faster.

Half a mile down the ridge, where Kabato remembered the overhanging rocky ledge, the Cascade River joined a tributary stream. The rushing water was now high up the rocky banks of the river, swollen by the melting snow and recent torrents of rain. Chunks of ice bobbed in the swift current and whirled in eddies below the rocks. Here the deer paused, but only for a moment. They must cross the rushing river or fall prey to the following wolves. One after another they plunged into the torrent, and, with the strength of desperation, each safely reached the other shore. One by one they disappeared into the gathering darkness of the forest beyond.

At the river the wolves also hesitated. They milled about the rocky bank as the snow swirled ever more thickly in the twilight. They feared the turbulent water, but appetite urged them on. The big old lead wolf was first to strike out across the river, followed closely by his mate and the rest of the pack. They were still in midstream, struggling against the current, when a large mass of ice that had jammed upstream broke loose with an extra surge of water. The grinding ice mass and surging current swept the wolves downriver as they bobbed helplessly in the torrent. A large chunk of ice struck one wolf, and he sank from sight while the others battled for their lives.

Deer, bears, and all else were forgotten as the wolves fought desperately to reach whatever shore they could. Some of the wolves clawed their way onto chunks of ice as the river carried them downstream. For a few minutes they were able to ride the ice in the surge of the flood waters; but soon the ice cake would circle in a swift eddy, dip, and sink, dumping the terrified wolf into the swirling water once more. Others were swept from their ice chunks by low-hanging branches above the river.

For more than two miles the roaring river swept the wolves along, until at last the banks grew farther apart, the torrent slackened, and downed trees and deadheads caught both the ice chunks and the weary wolves. One by one, each wet, bedraggled wolf pulled himself to shore. They were scattered miles apart along both sides of the river, too tired to be hungry or to try to find their family. Darkness had fallen, and the snow whirled all about as each wolf shook the water from his fur as best he could and sought a dry place in the brush to rest and sleep.

6. *The Den in the Hollow Pine*

As soon as the wolves had disappeared along the pine-ridge trail, out of sight and out of hearing, Kabato grunted to the cubs to come down from the pine tree. Never had the cubs been so eager to obey their mother. They both began to scramble down backward, but Anang was in such a hurry and his paws were so numb with cold that he lost his hold on the trunk and tumbled downward, bouncing from branch to branch. Each limb of the tree broke his fall a little, and at the bottom he landed right on his worried mother.

Halfway down Anoki too decided that falling was quicker and easier. She landed on the soft, rain-soaked pine needles, now covered with fresh new snow. Squeaking and shivering, she ran to join Anang and Kabato, who gathered both babies to her and inspected them anxiously. They were cold, wet, tired, hungry, frightened, and miserable—but unharmed. Kabato herself did not feel the cold or wet under her long thick fur, but she was very tired from her long battle with the wolves, and her leg was sore where the wolves had nipped her.

Most of all Kabato was anxious for her youngsters' safety. She knew she must find shelter for them at once. Darkness had fallen, the temperature was dropping fast, and the wind and snow now swirled in a raging blizzard. Kabato did not dare continue down the ridge toward the river and the rocky ledge she had remembered, for that was the way the wolves had gone. Herding the cubs close before her, she turned the other way along the ridge-top trail.

Soon they came to the giant white pine where the great horned owls were nesting. The tree was over six feet across at its base, with immense limbs broken by the wind and deep slashes where lightning had struck and slivered it. In the hollow top, some fifty feet up, the mother and baby owls were asleep in their nest. Down below, at the base of the tree, Kabato sniffed and scratched in the darkness at a small opening among the tree's spreading roots.

Digging quickly with her strong arms and claws, biting and tearing at the frozen earth and roots, Kabato enlarged the hole enough to admit her head and shoulders. Just as she had thought, the base of the tree was hollow, with only a shell of live wood on the outside. Digging, clawing, and biting with all her remaining strength, she soon had made an entrance large enough so that she could crawl into the hollow tree trunk. The bottom of the hollow was filled with rotted wood and sawdust, and in no time at all she had scooped out a soft, dry nest in the rotted pine.

All this time Anang and Anoki were huddled, cold and whimpering, where Kabato had left them under a dense spruce thicket nearby. Now Kabato called them to come at once. Emerging from the entrance, she grasped the two cubs and pushed them into the hollow tree. She crawled in after them and held them close to her. The cubs were icy cold and shivering, but Kabato was hot and steaming from her exertions in fighting the wolves and preparing the new nest.

Kabato knelt down with her head between her legs, nuzzling Anang and Anoki tenderly under her warm body. While the hungry cubs began to nurse, she licked each one all over until its fur was dry. Soon the cubs' contented little murmuring song began as they sucked their mother's sweet, nourishing milk and their bodies grew warm again. Their crooning song filled the dark, warm nest while the good milk filled their stomachs, and soon they were all three sound asleep in the hollow pine nest, the dangers and terrors of the long day at last forgotten.

It snowed all that night and the next day. The howling wind piled high drifts below the ridge, and even in level, protected places the snow lay two feet deep. But Kabato and the cubs were warm and cozy in their hollow-tree den. The snow had covered the entrance, but high up in the hollow trunk light and fresh air filtered in through knotholes and crevices.

The second morning dawned clear and cold. Rays of sunlight penetrated from high above down into the bears' warm den. By now Kabato had recovered from her exertions and her wound was healing, and the cubs were ready to explore their new home. The loose sawdust on the floor was perfect for tumbling about on, and the tall hollow trunk beckoned them upward. They had just begun to climb a vertical ridge that ran up the inside of the trunk when they heard a strange sound from above. "Kuk . . . kuk . . . kuk," called a harsh voice, and then began a great knocking and pounding on one side of the tree. The hollow pine echoed and re-echoed with the hammering, while Anang and Anoki huddled together in alarm and Kabato slept soundly through the commotion.

Silence fell for a moment, then "Kuk . . . kuk" came the call again, and more hammering, this time on the opposite side of the tree. Bits of sawdust and dead bark showered down on the startled cubs as they wondered who could be trying to tear down their house. Suddenly still more bits of dead wood tumbled down, and a new shaft of sunlight appeared some ten feet up the trunk. The big long bill and bright red crest of a pileated woodpecker appeared in the oblong hole. He looked

down at the cubs as curiously as they looked up at him. Then
he went methodically about his business, prying off pieces of
rotten wood with his powerful bill in search of white grubs for
his breakfast.

Reassured, the cubs continued exploring their new home in
the giant white pine. For about twelve feet up from the ground
the trunk was hollow, though lined with vertical ridges of
sound or partly rotted wood. Here and there a ledge extended
from one ridge to another, and these made perfect places for
the cubs to play. Anoki would scramble up one ridge and
Anang up another, in a contest to see which could get to the
ledge first. Then they boxed and wrestled, each trying to tum-
ble the other off the narrow platform. In the end the rotten
wood crumbled beneath them, or both lost their balance together, dropping down one after another onto the soft sawdust
floor or landing on their sleeping mother.

Anoki learned to work her way up two ridges that were too
narrow to climb, by bracing her body between them and inch-
ing upward like an inchworm. Anang was a little too big and
clumsy to duplicate her feat, but he consoled himself by finding a hollow limb to hide in, way at the top of the hollow
trunk. It was several days before Anoki finally discovered his
secret hideout. Then they would hide there together, teasing
their mother when she woke and looked for them.

The days passed in happy play inside the hollow pine, and
each day the cubs grew bigger and stronger. Their fuzzy black
fur grew longer and covered their bodies more thickly, the
better to protect them from cold and rain and from summer

heat and insects. Their teeth had begun to appear, and their sturdy small bodies had started to catch up in size with their big paws and stand-up ears.

Kabato was proud of her babies' healthy growth and seldom scolded them for their noisy, rambunctious play. Only when they climbed too far out of sight, or woke her just once too often, would she growl sternly and cuff them to quiet obedience. In spite of her rough discipline, she was as tender and loving as any mother could be. When she rolled on her back, she always took care that neither cub was under her; and lying on her back, with all four feet in the air, she often joined in their games, tossing the cubs in the air with her feet, catching them in midair, and passing them from forefeet to hindfeet in a dizzy game of catch till Anang and Anoki were breathless and squealing with delight.

In spite of all the squealing, growling, crooning, and snoring in the bears' den below, the great horned owls in the top of the giant pine did not seem in the least disturbed. The hollow stub where the owls were nesting was more than forty feet above the hollow base of the trunk where Kabato had made her den, and there was no passageway between. Red squirrels and chickadees also used the giant pine's knotholes and crevices, and though they were wary of the owls, peace reigned in the big hollow tree for many days.

Late one afternoon toward the end of March, the peace was suddenly broken. Anang and Anoki had climbed up to their hiding place in the hollow branch and had fallen asleep while waiting for Kabato to wake up and look for them. As they drowsed and nodded, there came a quick scratching and chittering in the pine boughs outside. A fisher, one of the rarest and shyest animals of the north woods, was chasing a red squirrel through the pine tops.

Pekan the fisher was a slim and agile hunter, nearly three feet long from nose to tail and covered with thick blackish fur. He ran and leaped through the treetops with great speed, almost as sure-footed as little Chickaree, the red squirrel he was chasing. Chattering frantically, Chickaree raced along a branch of the giant pine, searching for a knothole to hide in.

Near the base of the hollow branch where Anang and Anoki were napping, the red squirrel found a knothole just her size. In she darted, squeaking with fear, and scampered right over the drowsing cubs. The startled young bears woke up so suddenly they lost their balance, and down they all tumbled into the dark den, squirrel and cubs together, squeaking and squealing, to land right smack on longsuffering Kabato. Just then the hungry fisher found a pileated woodpecker hole he could squeeze into. Hot on the scent of the little red squirrel, he took a flying leap downward, lighting right on Kabato's stomach in the darkness.

This was too much even for good-tempered Kabato. With a mighty growl that shook the hollow old tree, the mother bear reared up in anger, looking for the intruders who dared to disturb her and her cubs. Sawdust flew as the terrified fisher raced round and round, searching for an exit, while Kabato swiped at him with her sharp claws and Anang and Anoki squealed and scrambled to stay out of the way.

In all the excitement, little Chickaree lost no time in darting out another knothole and away across the forest, long before the groggy fisher managed to find the woodpecker hole once more and make his escape. Poor Pekan was much chastened as he loped off through the snow, for he had few enemies in the forest and was not used to such rough treatment. The red squirrel had escaped, and Pekan was still hungry; but he was soon rewarded by finding a porcupine trail.

The broad, wallowing tracks in the snow were still fresh and led to a big spruce tree. In his slow, plodding way the porcupine had climbed nearly to the top of the tree and now was girdling the trunk as he ate his fill of tender bark. In a flash the fisher had climbed the spruce and tumbled the porcupine to the ground. The porcupine slapped his tail on the fisher's neck and back, filling the skin with spiny quills, but Pekan did not hesitate. He flipped the porcupine on his back, tore open the soft, unprotected underside, and ate till he could hold no more.

Few other animals in the forest would dare to attack a porcupine as the fisher had done, for the porcupine's sharp quills can penetrate deeply into most animals' bodies until they reach a vital organ and cause death. But the fisher has an invisible armor against the porcupine's quills—a tough, plastic-like membrane under the skin. The quills cannot penetrate this membrane but travel instead just under the skin until they emerge once more at the surface and drop off.

In this way Nature has provided a balance for life in the forest. If it were not for the fisher's armor against quills, the porcupines, who have few other enemies, would become too plentiful and destroy the forests by girdling and killing many pine and spruce trees. Today there are few fishers left in the northern woodlands, for man and his traps and logging have destroyed many of these valuable animals. Only when man and Nature work in harmony, maintaining the natural balance of the animals and trees of the forest, can all God's creatures survive and enjoy the beauty and freedom of the north woods.

7. The Coming of Spring

Spring came late that year in northern Minnesota. After the
March blizzard, the cold hung on day after day. But the sun
rose higher and earlier, and its rays were warmer, and everywhere in the woods the stir of new life was felt. Tara the otter
gave birth to her babies in a den in the rock cliff above the
Cascade River, and Pekan the fisher's mate had couched a
new family in a cedar stub in the middle of the swamp.

It was the time of mating travel for the skunks. Their tracks
appeared in the snow all along the ridge trail as they journeyed
day and night, unafraid of forest enemies. But the great horned
owls in their nest above the bear den watched the skunks with
hungry eyes. The two little owlets were growing bigger and
greedier every day, and it took many mice and rabbits, shrews

and voles to keep them satisfied. And the owls loved skunk meat, no matter what the price. More than once the bear cubs heard and smelled the battle outside as Bubo the owl swooped down to attack a skunk and was sprayed and blinded by its pungent scent before he could gorge on the sweet meat.

On sunny days the chickadees and nuthatches flitted through the sunflecked woods. "Ki-wi, ki-wi" rang the chickadees' plaintive spring song, and "yank, yank" answered the nuthatches in their soft nasal voices. In late April came the first long warm spell. A soft south wind blew along the ridge, bringing the smells of moist pine needles and forest duff where the snow had melted. The first flights of ducks winged northward overhead, looking for patches of open water, and redwinged blackbirds returned to the cedar swamp. "Conk-a-ree" they sang, swaying in the highest alder tops, singing the sweet spring music of the marshes.

Each day seemed warmer than the one before, but the snow still lingered in the deep woods. It settled and contracted under the dark spruce boughs, and the high drifts steadily shrank; but only on the southern slopes had it disappeared entirely. There the sleeping woodchucks felt the sun's warmth and woke to open and clean their burrows. Ruffed grouse walked in slow and stately steps across the clearings, picking at last fall's berries revealed beneath the snow.

As the ice retreated from the edges of the northern lakes, suckers and northern pike began to gather in the newly opened pools, ready to travel up the streams to spawn. Beavers greeted the newly opened water with happy splashes and, in the mild,

lengthening evenings, swam short distances from their lodges
to cut young poplars for a taste of fresh bark.

In the giant pine on the ridge Kabato too felt the call of
spring in the air, but she was in no hurry to leave their warm,
dry den. Each day Anang and Anoki grew more restless and
eager to explore the world beyond their den. But each time
they ventured out the entrance in the roots, Kabato's stern
grunts soon called them back, and they dared not disobey.
Patiently Kabato dozed the hours away. A late April cold
spell was followed by a thaw and warm rain. Now the snow
melted fast, till nearly all the ridge and every hillside lay clear.

On the last day in April, when the sun was high and the
bare ground on the ridge trail was nearly dry, Kabato stretched
and yawned, sniffed the warm air outside the den, and crawled
at last out into the bright sunshine. Wild with excitement,
Anang and Anoki scrambled after her. For a moment they all
blinked and squinted in the blinding sunlight. Then, as their
eyes grew used to the light, the cubs began to roll and somersault in the fragrant pine needles while Kabato stretched again
and sniffed in all directions, using all her bear instincts and remembered wisdom to plan her family's course.

Kabato knew the time for long sleep and rest was over. Her
cubs were so active now that they could not be content in the
den. It was time to travel, time to find food again for herself
and gradually to teach the young ones to find and eat more
than their mother's milk. The cubs had grown strong and
sturdy in the three months since their birth, and they must
learn now to travel and be at home in the wide wilderness.

Anang weighed nearly eight pounds and Anoki seven. They were no longer homely babies but had grown to be attractive youngsters, more appealing than any toy Teddy bears and far more lively. It would be another year at least before they could leave their mother, and three years before they reached full adult growth. But already they were leaving babyhood and ready to learn the ways of adult bears.

Kabato herself looked little changed after her long winter fast. Although she had not eaten or drunk since last November, she seemed as fat and sleek as before. Her stomach had shrunk to a small ball no bigger than a man's fist, and she still felt no hunger. But nursing the cubs for three months without water had left her dehydrated. She felt a great thirst, and, calling the cubs to follow, she started up the ridge trail. Soon she found a small creek rushing down the steep slope, and, kneeling down, she drank and drank until her distended stomach could hold no more.

Now Kabato sniffed the air again, rising tall on her hind legs to look both ways along the pine ridge and catch whatever scents the spring breeze might carry. Instinctively she turned north, following the deer trail along the ridge away from the Cascade River and deeper into the wilderness. The ridge ran northeastward for several miles, and Kabato led the cubs along it at an easy pace. Anang and Anoki trotted eagerly behind, stopping now and then to roll in the pine needles or wrestle with each other in sheer high spirits. When they grew tired and hungry, Kabato stopped to let them nurse and rest, but she herself still felt no urge to eat.

They slept that night in a nest of pine needles under a thick spruce grove. In the morning they moved on along the ridge. The trail was well worn by many deer hoofs, but other animals had used it too—wolves and foxes, martens and fishers, rabbits, skunks, weasels, and bobcats, as well as bears. The second afternoon Anoki had run on ahead, impatient as always, when around a fallen log in the trail came a mother porcupine and her baby. The baby waddled behind the mother, grunting happily, "Unk . . . unk . . . unk." Now and then he climbed up his mother's tail and back and clasped her neck. Strangely enough, no quills seemed to prick the baby, and the mother plodded placidly on, dragging her bristling tail along the ground.

Anoki was fascinated by these spiny creatures and ventured closer. The mother porcupine stopped short and grunted sharply. Dutifully her baby retreated to a spot behind his mother's tail. Anoki was delighted with the little creature and, circling the angry mother, she put out a curious paw to touch the baby's tiny tail. Slap! went the mother's tail and baby's both at once, and poor Anoki howled with fright and pain. Two quills struck her right front paw, and though one fell out, the other lodged quite deeply.

In one bound Kabato appeared around the log, alarmed at Anoki's outcry. With a stern cuff Kabato slapped Anoki away from the bristling porcupines and, giving them a wide berth, herded the two cubs quickly down the trail. She had learned long ago to leave porcupines alone, and now Anoki had learned that lesson too in a very painful way. With her teeth she

pulled out part of the quill, but the broken barb remained in her paw, reminding her for days to come that bears must learn to be cautious.

Three days after leaving the giant hollow pine, Kabato found a clump of spruces and jack pine higher on the slope. A new craving urged her to climb the smaller jack pines and nibble on the tender bark and needles. She also dug and ate some spruce roots and spruce bark, and soon the aromatic medicines started her digestive juices flowing. Hunger began to stir in her for the first time in many months. Leaving the ridge, she looked for a low, marshy spot in the forest. There she dug the pungent roots of skunk cabbage and jack-in-the-pulpit and ate them with great relish.

Now she was truly "as hungry as a bear," It seemed she could not eat enough to satisfy her hunger. Wandering from ridge to marsh to ridge again, she fed avidly on roots and new grass, bark and aspen buds, leaves, last year's berries, and any beetles, grubs, and ants she found beneath the rocks and rotten logs. Even though she ate and ate, Kabato now began to lose her winter fat. Her increased activity and forest travels, along with the nursing of the ever-bigger cubs, made far greater demands on her body than her long winter rest. Within a month there would be little fat left on her sturdy frame, and she would spend most of the spring and summer days searching for food for herself and her cubs.

Anang and Anoki followed Kabato's every move, sniffing curiously at the strange food she ate, but it did not tempt them. Sometimes they nibbled experimentally at a white grub or shred of bark, but they much preferred their mother's rich, warm milk. While she fed they gamboled all about her, boxing, playing tag, and rolling in the spongy brown pine needles.

Sometimes their play grew rough and quarrels brewed. Anoki had a quick temper. When Anang teased her or hurt her accidentally, she fought back in earnest, biting and clawing her brother till he ran behind Kabato for protection. When Anoki rushed after him, growling and squalling, Kabato would end the quarrel as quickly as it had begun. Each cub received a swat from her powerful paw, and two chastened youngsters crept away, ready to be friends again. Kabato's discipline seemed harsh at times, but she knew the cubs must learn the rules of survival in the wild. Kabato's own behavior taught them by example, and their playtime was a learning time as well.

8. Bear Tree and Bee Tree

During their first week of travel, Kabato and the cubs moved gradually northeastward along the long pine ridge. Kabato slowed her pace to match the cubs', taking plenty of time to feed and let the youngsters play. Whenever Anang and Anoki grew tired or hungry, the family stopped to rest in a sheltered spot beneath a balsam thicket or in a brushy clearing. Kabato dozed while the youngsters nursed and napped, but soon she called them to follow her, always eager to move on. They traveled partly by day and partly by night, resting, feeding, and exploring the woodlands.

The ridge extended nearly ten miles beyond the cedar swamp where Kabato had made her winter den. White and Norway pines covered the crest, while balsams, birches, and aspens grew lower on the slopes and on the level land beyond. Below the ridge a chain of small lakes and streams drained southeastward to join the Cascade River in its rocky rush downward to Lake Superior. Marshy brushland and clumps of alders fringed many of the smaller ponds, and ducks and bitterns were already seeking nests in these secluded waters.

To the north the land rose sharply in slanting granite ledges. These were the Sawtooth Mountains, their jagged forest-covered ridges hiding the long, rockbound lakes that lay between the sawteeth. Less than ten miles from the end of the ridge Kabato and the cubs were traveling, the rocky Misquah Hills rose over two thousand feet to form the highest point in Minnesota.

Seven days after they had left the den in the hollow pine, Kabato and the cubs came to the end of the ridge. Long ago a glacier had pushed up the sand and gravel that composed the ridge, leaving an abrupt slope downward when the ice sheet melted. The game trail turned southward here, leading down to a small reed-fringed lake. Here too the pines thinned out, affording a wide view to the north and west.

The panorama of sky, lakes, woods, and rocky hills meant little to Kabato, but the scent of a large aspen at the end of the ridge trail interested her greatly. Rearing on her hind legs, she sniffed the trunk of the tree eagerly, clasping it with her forepaws and digging her claws into the bark. Her keen nose told her that this was a bear tree, used as a signpost and bulletin board by all black bears who passed this way. The bark was torn and scarred by many bear teeth and claws, and bits of black fur clung to rough places on the trunk. Each adult bear would rub and scratch his back against the tree, leaving his scent, then reach as high up the trunk as he could to make his claw marks.

As Kabato sniffed the bear tree, she caught a scent that stirred her memories. Surely that was the scent of Koda, her own mate and her babies' father, whom she had not seen through all the fall and winter months. The odor clung faintly to the bark, so elusive that it must have been two weeks or more since he passed by. Excitedly Kabato sniffed and peered high up the tree. Way up the trunk, several inches above the other claw marks, there were the freshly made tall slashes that were Koda's mark, the mark of the largest bear in the region.

Many impulses stirred in Kabato. Eagerly she rubbed her back and head against the bear tree, leaving her own scent and bits of shedding fur; and patiently she let the curious cubs sniff the tree that held such interest for their mother. If she had been alone, Kabato might have tried to follow Koda's trail, seeking her mate once more. But she was not alone, and all her maternal instincts told her "No." Her first thoughts now were always for Anoki and Anang, and the cubs would need all her care and attention for many months. Even good-tempered Koda might grow irritable and jealous in their presence, for adult male bears are solitary creatures most of the year, and mother bears wisely keep their young cubs out of father's way.

Kabato could not tell which way Koda had gone; but the trail most animals used turned southward at the end of the ridge. Kabato turned north. Grunting to the cubs to follow, she left the trail and scrambled down the gravelly slope. Their way now led through balsam and aspen groves and hillsides covered with white birches. In the early May sunshine the white birch and pale aspen branches gleamed against the blue sky, still leafless, and blue hepaticas and white anemones poked their flower stems above the leaf mold on the woodland floor. Here Kabato showed the youngsters how to find tiny mice and shrews beneath dead logs and rotting stumps. Catching these small creatures seemed great fun to the cubs, but they let Kabato eat them by herself, taking only an experimental nibble or two for themselves.

As Kabato hunted she heard a humming sound overhead,

and when she looked up she saw that there were many bees flying about in the warm May sunshine gathering pollen from the birch and aspen catkins. Bees made Kabato think at once of honey, the forest food she liked best of all. Guided by their buzzing, she followed their flight to a large hollow birch tree where the bees were cleaning out their hive. Dead bees lay on the ground about the tree, and more kept falling from a large woodpecker hole about ten feet above the ground.

Swiftly Kabato climbed the hollow tree and tore at the bees' entrance with her claws and teeth. The rotted wood gave way easily, and angry bees swarmed out to protest. The bees crawled all over Kabato's head and body, looking for places to sting her through her heavy fur. On her nose and on her belly, where the fur had been rubbed away by the nursing cubs, the bees stung Kabato unmercifully. But the prospect of honeycomb and bee grubs made the pain worth bearing.

When the bees realized that Kabato would soon reach their honey hoard, they gathered on the comb, eating all they could hold, in hopes of carrying away in their bodies enough to keep them and their queen while they established another place to live. Soon the rotten wood was entirely torn away. Kabato gorged on the sweet honey, eating the brood cells of the comb as well and the grubs that would have hatched into worker bees. She even ate the bees that clung to the comb, feasting until comb, honey, grubs, and all were gone.

Bits of the sweet honeycomb had fallen to the ground, and now Kabato backed down the tree and called the cubs to come and taste it. They had been watching from a distance, where

their mother had left them sitting in the bracken, and they approached with caution. Anang smelled the sweet honey on Kabato's coat and began to lick it eagerly, while Anoki found the bits of sticky comb were equally delicious. This was the first grown-up food they liked as much as milk, and they ate the comb fragments eagerly. Anoki got a mouthful of stinging bees along with her honeycomb, and she squealed in pain. But the pleasant sweetness made the stings seem unimportant, and both cubs searched the ground till every single grub and bee and piece of comb was eaten.

9. Fishing with the Otters

When they had all licked themselves clean, Kabato led the way northward once more. They were reaching the higher ridges now, and many little streams rushed down the rocky hillsides. Kabato slowed her pace as the climb became steeper, and she stopped often to let the cubs rest. They slept several nights in a cave beneath a rocky ledge, feeding by day on the bearberries that carpeted the groves of straight and slender young Norway pines. The glossy leaves of wintergreen and white bunchberry blooms made patches of spring color among the red-barked pines, and blueberries that would ripen later were already setting buds.

In the rushing streams rainbow trout and lampreys were working their way up the rapids to spawn. The lampreys are parasitic eel-like creatures, one to two feet long, which cling with sucker-like mouths to larger fish and slowly kill them. Each spring the lampreys migrate up the rivers from Lake Superior to lay their eggs in the shallow upland pools. Here the lamprey larvae hatch and bury themselves in mud, waiting for five years before they become adult and return to Lake Superior to prey on the lake trout and whitefish.

The stream below the rock den where the bears had slept was full of lampreys. One morning Kabato heard a flock of ravens croaking and calling a little way upstream. A fresh, fishy smell was in the air, and Kabato decided to investigate. The cubs were big enough now so that no raven would dare attack them, and Kabato knew the raven cries and fishy smell meant food.

Picking their way along the high banks of the stream, Kabato and the cubs soon found the reason for the ravens' conclave. A group of four yearling otters were fishing for lampreys and frolicking on the banks, catching many of the eel-like creatures in their jaws and leaving them half-eaten at the top of the steep slope. The ravens perched in the nearby pines, dropping down whenever they dared, to seize a dead

lamprey and flap off with it for dinner. Each lamprey the otters killed meant fewer new ones born to threaten Minnesota's fish. Thus, in their carefree way, the otters worked to maintain Nature's balance and conserve our valuable game fish.

Not only the ravens but Kabato too appreciated the otters' catch. She sniffed a lamprey, chewed it, and found it good to eat. She knew the otters posed no danger to her cubs, so she ignored them and settled down to eat her fill. Anoki and Anang nibbled at the lampreys cautiously, but when one of them writhed and flopped in Anoki's face, she dropped it hastily.

Both cubs were much more interested in the young otters' antics. Their sleek, furry brown bodies with short legs and webbed feet were built more for swimming than for walking, yet they moved with ease and a lithe grace both on shore and in the water. In a pool below the rapids they dived and swam like porpoises, playing tag, chasing lampreys, and carrying them up the steep banks. At the top of the bank the otters abandoned their catch and slid gaily on their bellies down the steep slope and back into the water without a splash.

With great good humor they tried to tempt Anoki and Anang to join their games. Four sleek otter heads peeked over the bank, chuckling in a friendly fashion; then four long, furry bodies loped around the cubs, sniffing and grunting in otter talk, inviting the cubs to slide and swim with them. The cubs were fascinated by these playful yearlings, but native caution held them back. Anang looked toward his mother for

instructions; but Kabato knew the cubs were safe and let them make their own decision.

At last Anang got up his courage. Approaching the edge of the bank, he peered down the otter slide at the frolic below. He whined invitingly, hoping they would come up and play with him, and right away the whole troupe galloped up the bank. Delighted with this roly-poly playmate, they tumbled all about him till suddenly, before he knew it, Anang was tumbling with them, head over heels, right down the otter slide. He hit the water with a splash and came up, sputtering, several feet from the shore. Too startled to be frightened, he kicked hard with his arms and hindlegs, making a tremendous commotion but managing to keep afloat and move toward shore. Once he got started, he swam instinctively, as if he had always known how.

Anang lost no time in scrambling up the bank, however, and he ran straight to Kabato for comfort and reassurance. But Kabato was not alarmed in the least. It was as good a time as any for the cubs to learn to swim, so she just snuffed and sniffed and kept on eating. Saucy Anoki gamboled over to tease her wet, bedraggled brother, but she was careful to keep her distance from the otters. Maybe Anang had learned to swim, but even venturesome Anoki was not ready to duplicate his feat on purpose. From now on both cubs were content to watch from a distance while their otter playmates tumbled and rolled and raced and splashed in a frenzy of joy among the woodland rocks and waters.

10. Koda

By noon Kabato had had her fill of lampreys. She called the cubs and ambled on upstream. Half a mile beyond the otters' playground, the swift stream broadened into a little lake. As they came around a boulder on the bank, Kabato stopped short. Obediently the cubs behind her froze in their tracks, knowing that their mother's stance meant possible danger ahead.

On the south shore of the lake a huge black bear was fishing from a sloping rock. Northern pike were spawning in the shallow waters near the shore, and the big bear was intent upon them. He waited patiently till one strayed too close to his rock, then fell upon it with his heavy body and caught it in his teeth. After wading to shore, he tore the fish apart, ate it with relish, and returned to his position on the rock to wait again.

Kabato was downwind from the fishing bear. He was too far away for her to see clearly his big brown-furred head and massive black body, but the scent that drifted to her on the warm May breeze she would recognize anywhere. It was Koda, her mate, whom she had tried so hard to avoid. He too must have turned north instead of south from the ridge trail, seeking the deeper wilderness where bears could roam and forage undisturbed by man and his civilization.

With a low, urgent grunt Kabato ordered Anang and Anoki to climb the nearest big tree, a tamarack that grew in the boggy lowland at the outlet of the lake. The cubs obeyed without question, clambering up branch after branch till they reached a high vantage point. From the tall tamarack the cubs could see the big bear in the distance, and they were filled with curiosity and excitement. They had never seen another bear before, except their mother, and this mysterious giant seemed marvelous and strange to them. They knew from their mother's behavior that this huge stranger meant something special to her and therefore to themselves as well; but they could not know he was their own father.

Anang especially was fascinated by the big bear fishing on the lake shore. He sniffed the air repeatedly, as he had often seen his mother do, catching Koda's scent as it drifted downwind. It was the same scent he remembered on the bear tree on the pine ridge, where his mother had sniffed and clawed and rubbed the bark with such great interest. Somehow the

scent of this giant male bear seemed wonderful and important
to Anang, more important than anything in the world, and he
longed to approach the stranger. He wanted to watch him fish
and forage, to inspect him and find out all about him. But no
matter how much he wanted to, Anang knew he must not
leave the tamarack. Kabato had given her orders, and she
must be obeyed.

With the cubs safely hidden in the treetop, Kabato silently
disappeared into the forest. Walking softly as a shadow, keeping always downwind and behind the dark pine trunks, she
soundlessly approached within a hundred feet of Koda. Having
crept to the edge of a rocky outcrop, she could look down
on him, unseen and unheard, from behind the rocks.

For many minutes Kabato crouched on the high rocks in

perfect silence, watching intently as Koda fished. Her mind and heart remembered much about this big brown-headed mate of hers—his gentleness to her, the playful games they had together, his strength and skill in hunting food and fishing, and, most of all, his peaceful nature and good temper, which made him far less quarrelsome than many male bears and earned him much good will among his woodland neighbors.

Kabato remembered much, but many parts of Koda's story she could never know. She could not know about his birth and early life, how he came to have his unusual brown and black markings, how he had grown to be the largest black bear in the region, or why his nature was so kind and gentle. That story had begun seven years earlier, when Koda was born near the shores of Northern Light Lake in the Quetico wilderness of Ontario, Canada, less than fifty miles north of where he was fishing today.

Koda was born in the winter of the Big Snow in southern Ontario. It snowed almost every day that winter, and sunshine was a rarity. More than 240 inches had fallen by the end of March, each fall packing down the snow beneath as more weight was added. The many feet of snow on the ground caused great hardship for many north-woods creatures, but far worse was yet to come.

Late in March the first prolonged warm spell beckoned many of the early spring bird migrants northward to their Canadian nesting grounds. Flock after flock of bluebirds, horned larks, and snow buntings flew over the northern lakes and spruce forests, filling the air with their joyous calls and the sound of their wings. The wilderness resounded with the happy return of thousands and thousands of these songbirds welcoming the early spring, eager to reach their nesting areas.

Without warning disaster struck. Moist air brought by warm south winds from the Gulf of Mexico formed a great layer of dense clouds over the northern forests. The next morning dawned with an ominous red sky, the cloudbank glowing crimson almost to the sky's zenith. Soon rain began to fall in torrents and the wind shifted to the east, bringing cold air and a swift drop in temperature. Within an hour the rain had turned to sleet, freezing as soon as it reached the ground. Now the forests were coated with solid ice that built up layer after layer as the sleet continued to fall. Trees, snow, rocks, and all living creatures were locked in a terrible icy prison.

The migrating bluebirds were driven to the ground, seeking shelter under thickets of conifers. But many thousands died, with no food to be found and their wings too coated with ice to fly. Some of the winter birds and the migrants who took shelter in hollow trees survived. Grubs and insects in the rotting wood provided them with food, but if the holes in the trees were on the east side of the trunk they soon became iced over by the sleet-laden east wind, and the helpless birds were trapped with no way to escape.

Many ruffed grouse and spruce grouse which had slanted into the deep snow to sleep were caught by the ice in their snowy beds and never again saw the light of day. The deer yards were a glassy maze of icy paths, too slick for the deer to find footing when chased by their enemies the wolves. Only the fact that the woods were strewn with dead birds for the wolves to feast on saved the deer from near annihilation.

Next to the birds, the trees of the northern forests suffered most grievously. The thick ice coating placed a heavy burden on their boughs, and the evergreens especially were damaged by the wind and frozen rain. Ice-laden limbs snapped and broke, and trees fell with every gust of wind. It seemed as if Satan himself were stalking the northland that spring, bent on destroying all birds and trees and wildlife in his icy grasp. The creatures that sought shelter underneath the cedar, spruce, and balsam thickets fared the best; but the toll of many species —especially the lovely bluebirds—was so great that ten years passed before they began to appear once more in the northland.

The great ice storm had a profound effect on Koda's life. During the height of the storm a large ice-laden elm crashed down at the edge of a swamp on Southeast Bay of Northern Light Lake. The tree's big scraggly limbs snapped and shattered as it fell, and the sharp stubs penetrated the ice, snow, and earth beneath the trunk. One of these stubs struck deep into the underground den of a large mother bear and her twin cubs. Koda was one of those twins, a big ten-pound, three-month-old baby with a cinnamon-brown head and face topping his husky, black-furred body. The falling tree stub missed Koda by a hair's breadth, but his poor little sister was buried deep beneath its weight.

For a long time the mother bear dug frantically in the shambles of her den, searching for her lost cub, while Koda whimpered in the icy snow nearby. But the mother bear searched in vain. At last she knew she must give up her efforts and find shelter for her one surviving baby. She held Koda close to her, warming him and comforting his misery, though she herself was stunned with loss and cut and bruised by the crashing tree.

Through the long night and next day Koda's mother slowly made her way five miles over the ice-glazed snow, carrying Koda where he could not walk, to a cave in a rocky cliff along the lake. There she made a safe, warm nest for Koda, her one remaining cub, on whom she lavished all her love and attention.

Here on the rocky lake shore Koda thrived and grew throughout the spring and early summer. With all the milk and other foods meant for two cubs, he grew far larger and stronger than average. His unusual coloring, inherited partly from his cinnamon-brown father and partly from his black-furred mother, also set him apart from other cubs his age. Without his sister for a playmate, Koda was often lonely and longed for friends to romp with. But his mother loved him dearly, played with him often, and taught him all the bear wisdom that she knew. Thus Koda grew up with a sunny disposition, eager to be friends with all his neighbors in the northland.

One day in the summer of his first year Koda's mother led him to a big blueberry barren where several mother bears and their cubs were feeding. On the sunny slope ten little cubs were playing together, more bear cubs than Koda had ever

seen. He was so excited and delighted to see these possible playmates that he forgot all about the blueberries. For a long time he watched intently as the other youngsters wrestled and played tag. He longed to join in their game, approaching as close as he dared and whining a wistful plea for an invitation.

For some time the other cubs ignored the big brown-headed youngster. Then suddenly, as if on signal, the ten little cubs turned and raced toward Koda, bowling him over on his back, playfully nipping his toes and ears, and piling on top of him until he was completely covered by a squealing, grunting mound of furry bodies. When Koda got his wind back he joined the squealing and nipping enthusiastically and wrestled and pushed till the pile of cubs broke up as suddenly as it had formed.

This was Koda's initiation into the cub pack. After that he needed no further invitation to join in their romps as he so dearly wished to. All through the summer and fall he met the cubs often at the raspberry and blackberry patches, and later at the wild-cherry trees and under the scrub oaks where they fed on acorns. Now that he knew he had friends of his own age and kind all through the forests, he was not so lonely. But he always kept the gentle, friendly nature that had been bred in him by his loving mother's constant attention and by his childhood longing for a playmate.

11. Koda's Travels

When Koda and his mother came out of their winter den in his second spring, Koda was almost as big as his three-hundred-pound mother. He was still only a yearling and far from full-grown; but as they traveled together that spring Koda grew more and more skilled in all the ways of bears for finding food, shelter, and safe passage in the wilderness.

In the spring they browsed on skunk cabbage and on the cinnamon-fern tops that were just emerging from the moist woodland leaf mold. Koda was especially fond of the cinnamon ferns and ate them by the acre. He learned the best ways to catch the different kinds of fish, feasting on rainbow trout and suckers in the spring and catching brook trout in the fall as they spawned in the spring-fed streams. Koda's mother would lie across the little rills, damming the channel with her big body until the water spread and overflowed the stream's low banks. In the shallow pools formed by the overflow Koda chased the trout, catching them easily in the shallows. When the mother bear got up, releasing the dammed-up water, still more trout were stranded on the banks as the water flowed back to its channel. Koda would eat his fill of the good fish, relishing each mouthful, and he soon became one of the most skillful fishermen in the forests.

Through most of his second summer Koda roamed the Quetico lakes, woods, and marshes with his mother. During July she left him more often by himself while she disappeared into the forest. It was her mating time, and time for Koda to go his way alone. One hot day while he was swimming in the cool waters of Madalaine Lake, near his home territory, Koda's mother silently left her big brown-headed youngster for the last time. He was far bigger and more mature than most young bears are when they leave their mothers, and she knew it was best for them both to part. Next winter she would have new cubs to care for, and Koda must start learning now to live alone.

During his first weeks on his own Koda's loneliness was hard to bear. He had lost his sister long ago, and now his mother too. His young cub playmates of last summer were also living alone now and were scattered through the forests, no longer so easy to find for romps and games in the berry patches. But Koda's friendly nature did not allow him to mope or mourn for long. The north woods were full of bird and animal life, and Koda soon found new kinds of companion-ship.

Since early cubhood Koda had felt a special kinship with the birds. Perhaps it was because they all had suffered through the great ice storm; perhaps because their gay, free movements stirred Koda's playful spirit. Whatever the reason, Koda had always loved to watch the chickadees and nuthatches who crept and flitted boldly near him as they and he together searched old logs and hollow trees for grubs and beetles. Wood-peckers, finches, kinglets, and warblers—all the birds were his friends, and he had never harmed one in his life.

Now in September, when Koda was all alone, the birds of the northern woods and waters were his best companions. When he had fished and eaten berries till he could hold no more, he loved to lie on the lake shore, watching the loons and terns, the wheeling gulls migrating slowly southward, the flocks of ducks and geese resting and feeding before their long autumn flight.

Koda marveled as the geese, coming in from high in the sky, tipped, turned, and looped like falling leaves till they were near the water, then opened their wings and stayed their fall. Twice a day, at midmorning and midafternoon, the canvas-back ducks took their exercise. Koda lay on a point on Icarus Lake and watched them circle the lake, always crossing the point low, just above his head, flying faster than any of the other waterbirds, with rhythmic, steady wingbeats.

Flights of mallards coming in from the north set their wings, weaving from side to side as they broke ranks. "Cack . . . cack

. . . cack" rang their calls through the chill September air, and they plummeted downward almost to water level before they lifted their wings at the last instant and slowed to a safe landing.

One day late in September when Koda came out on the point, a large flock of whistling swans was feeding with the other waterfowl in a wild-celery bed. The great white birds probed the lake bottom with their long necks submerged, rooting up the wild-celery and sago pond roots. Now and then the smaller mudhens and mallards feeding nearby would steal a root the swans had brought to the surface, but the stately swans ignored this impertinence and continued to probe and feed unperturbed.

Koda watched the big birds in fascination. He longed to float as effortlessly as they did on the wide blue waters, and in his eagerness he waded out a long way into the shallow water, hoping to join them. The swans were not disturbed by the approach of this big brown-headed bear. They had seen grizzlies and brown bears even larger than Koda on their far-northern nesting grounds. But it was time for their afternoon exercises, and while Koda was still wading out to join them, the leader gave the signal to take off.

First one, then several, then all the whistling swans rose from the water laboriously. Their webbed feet pattered along the surface, and their wide wings at first barely lifted their heavy bodies. Then as they rose, their wingbeats struck a slow, methodical rhythm, becoming ever more powerful and effortless as they banked and circled into the wind, heading

straight for the shallows beyond the point where Koda stood watching, transfixed.

Koda reared on his hind legs, watching intently and longing to join in the flight. "Whoosh . . . whoosh . . . whoosh" went their serene, unhurried wingbeats, filling the air with their whistling sound as the whole flock flew no more than fifteen feet above Koda's head, their long necks outstretched and their great white wings flashing in the sunlight. Tipping back his head, Koda stared upward in delight as the swans passed over him, and as the last swan passed he toppled over backward in the water, kicking all four feet in the air.

Perhaps Koda sensed that this was the time that the birds flew south, leaving the northland for the long winter, and perhaps he still hoped somehow to join them. At any rate, soon afterward he began to travel toward the south. From Northern Light and Icarus Lakes the wilderness extended many miles in all directions, and south would do as well as north for a black bear to find food and fatten for the winter.

It was a good year for berries and wild fruit of all kinds, and Koda found plenty to eat as he wandered southward. Wild cherries and plums still hung from the trees, and acorns lay under the scrub oaks on open hillsides. These Koda ate with relish, along with roots and bark and ants and mice—and always, wherever he could find it, cinnamon fern. In shady, moist hollows it grew in profusion; in other places small clumps of sweet fern clung to rocky cliffs and ledges. Wherever Koda found it he reveled in its fragrance, not only eating it but rubbing his big brown head in its fronds or rolling in ecstasy in wide patches of it. The fern's sweet, pungent odor affected him as catnip does a cat, and he watched for it eagerly as he traveled.

In mid-October Koda crossed the international boundary between Canada and the United States. The border line runs through the long chain of lakes and rivers that separate Ontario and northern Minnesota; but in this wide wilderness neither man nor beast need know or care too much about such artificial boundaries. When Koda swam south across the narrows at the east end of Gunflint Lake, he could not know that he was entering another nation. The same vast, silent pine forests and rocky lake shores lay ahead as lay behind; and man had made few marks in recent years on this wild country.

Koda could not know, either, how fortunate he was to have been born in this region, one of the last remaining wilderness areas of our nation. The governments of the United States and Canada have agreed to keep a large tract of this border area forever roadless, without airplanes, and protected from timber-cutting, mining, hunting, trapping, and man's other exploitations. Here in the Quetico-Superior Wilderness Area man travels only by canoe or hiking, living close to Nature. Here man and Nature's other creatures can enjoy the lakes and forests on equal terms, respecting one another's rights and differences.

Even beyond the official roadless area, many miles of the Superior National Forest stretch out across northeastern Minnesota, sparsely settled and with few roads to mar the natural wild beauty of the north woods. Logging and lumbering are regulated to prevent the woods from being spoiled, and many stands of giant white and Norway pine still fringe the lake shores and the granite ridges. This was the vast wild country Koda roamed in his adulthood, wandering hundreds of miles through the forests, with seldom a glimpse of man or of his works.

The first road Koda ever saw was the winding gravel Gunflint Trail, the only road that approaches the border lake region. He crossed it quickly on his southward journey and spent the late fall feeding in the woods and marshes north of Muskeg Lake. In a den beneath a tangle of fallen spruces Koda spent his third winter, and in the spring and for the next three years he roamed the vast Superior Forest. North along the silent border lakes, the canoeists' paradise, east toward Grand Portage and the cliff-lined shore of Lake Superior, southwest from there toward Grand Marais, and west as far as Ely and the Echo Trail, Koda traveled at one time or another during his adult life. He first encountered man in his third year, east of Ely in November—deer-hunting season—and he learned then why man is shunned and feared by most forest dwellers.

Koda was heading back to his old winter den near Muskeg Lake when he met the strange two-legged creature on a trail. Friendly and curious, big Koda stood two-legged also, sniffing this new scent on the air, when "Crack! crack!" went the creature's strange long arm, and a bullet grazed Koda's shoulder with fiery speed. Startled and stung by pain, Koda could have crushed the foolish hunter with one blow of his mighty forepaw before the man could reload his gun, but Koda was no match for man in cruelty and wanton killing. The big brown-headed bear plunged deep into the forest, leaving the enemy whom he had never harmed as far behind as possible.

Koda's shoulder wound healed quickly, but he never forgot the bitter lesson of this encounter. His friendly nature had been betrayed, and he determined to avoid the territory of these treacherous creatures and all places that bore their scent. Koda was lucky to live in Minnesota, where no bounties are paid for killing bears, as in some states; but even in Minnesota bears may be killed by hunters in most counties at any season, not for meat and not because the bears are dangerous, but just because misguided people fear them. In his native wilderness the black bear does no harm to man and lives at peace with Nature. Only when man corrupts the black bear, luring him to garbage dumps, feeding and teasing him, betraying his trusting nature—only then is the black bear dangerous, through man's own folly.

Thus Koda learned that man was his enemy and the deep wilderness his safest home. For years he never came so close to man again, skirting the roads and lake-shore cabins and avoiding the campgrounds in the forest. In his fourth year he met Kabato, the sleekest young female he had ever seen, and their weeks of courtship were a time of joy for both.

Koda was full-grown at last, a giant of six hundred pounds, his distinctive brown-furred head contrasting with his powerful black body. Big as he was, he had never lost his friendly, playful spirit, and with Kabato for his mate, his long years of loneliness were over. They could not live together all the year, for that was not bear custom; but their paths crossed often in the forests, and every other year, when summer brought the mating season, they sought each other out for long and happy weeks together.

12. Paji

As Kabato watched Koda fishing on the lake shore she remembered their pleasant days together last July. She longed to let him know he was a father now to two fine cubs and let him see the youngsters she was so proud of. Crouching in silence on the high rocky ledge, she watched her big brown-headed mate and wished. Later, perhaps, when the cubs were bigger and needed less care—then might be the time for a happy family meeting. Bear instincts told Kabato she must wait, and soon she went away from the ledge as quietly as she had come, retracing her steps through the pines to the tall tamarack where she had left the cubs.

With a gentle grunt she called them down and nuzzled each one to make sure all was well. Anoki and Anang were wild with curiosity about their mother's disappearance. They knew somehow it had to do with the mysterious big fishing bear, and Anang yearned more than ever to run off and find him. But Kabato gave her marching orders straight away, and both cubs had to follow, no matter how they might fuss and grumble.

Kabato kept a brisk pace for an hour or more, bypassing the little lake and heading north once more. She wanted to put distance between the cubs and Koda, lest her own wishes tempt her to act unwisely. Soon Anoki and Anang began to whine and whimper, for they were hungry and it was hard to keep up with their mother. Several times Kabato stopped and waited for them to catch up, but each time she urged them on once more. Only when they had traveled two or three miles northward and crossed several streams and rocky ridges, did Kabato stop at last to let her youngsters nurse and rest.

The next day they moved at a more leisurely pace, still northward into the high Misquah Hills. As Kabato led the way along a well-used game trail they heard a whimper, like a baby's crying, from the underbrush a few yards off the trail. Kabato listened intently while Anang and Anoki looked about in wonder. The sound was just like their own crying when they were tired or hungry.

For a long moment Kabato hesitated. Surely that was a bear cub crying, yet there was no answering grunt or murmur from its mother. Kabato's maternal instincts were aroused, but she dared not interfere in the affairs of another mother bear. Just then the whining cry came again, so piteously that Kabato could not resist. With a warning cough she ordered Anoki and

Anang to climb the nearest tree while she turned off the trail
into the brush to investigate.

A little way off the trail, near a stream through the alder
brush, a baby bear was nuzzling its dead mother and crying
for milk. The cub was a little female, not black like her dead
mother, but covered with yellowish and reddish-brown fur.
She was about the same age as Anang and Anoki but smaller
and much more timid. When she saw Kabato she ran to the
nearest tree and climbed halfway up, frightened and crying,
yet hoping this strange mother bear had come to help.

Kabato approached with caution. The poor dead mother had been badly hurt, and the ground and brush were trampled with the marks of battle. The scent of bear was strong, but even stronger was the scent of moose, the largest animal that lived in these northern woods. Kabato's keen nose and knowledge of the forest told her much of the sad story. The mother of the cinnamon cub had left the trail to fish here in the stream. But at this very place a cow moose was hidden in the brush with her newborn calf. The wind had blown the bear's scent to the mother moose, and, fearing that the mother bear meant to attack her calf, she charged and caught the mother bear completely by surprise. One warning grunt was all the mother bear had time for, telling her little one to climb to safety, and then the angry moose had reared and struck a fatal blow with her large hoofed front feet. The mother bear's neck was broken instantly, yet the cow moose struck again and again, trampling the mother bear long after she was dead. Maddened by the threat she imagined to her baby, the moose ran first to her calf to nose and nuzzle it, and then to trample once more the long-dead mother bear.

Poor Paji, the little "yellow-hair" cub, clung all this time to her tree, terrified and crying. The moose seemed oblivious to the little bear cub, but at last, when the sun had set and darkness had fallen, she nudged her calf and led it off into the brush. Paji stayed up the tree all night, whining for her mother but afraid to come down. At daybreak she climbed down and tried to nudge and coax her mother back to life. But no milk came when she tried to nurse, and there was no warmth left in her mother's body. All day Paji had stayed close to her mother, crying to be fed. When Kabato appeared on the scene, she was so lonesome and hungry she was hardly even frightened of this stranger.

Kabato did not stay long in the trampled thicket. The tragedy that had occurred there made her uneasy for her own cubs' safety, and she wanted to get them away at once. She did not know what to do. Would her own cubs accept a strange adopted youngster, and could she give milk and find food enough for all? Grunting anxiously, Kabato turned back to the trail. When she reached the path she looked behind her, and there was Paji, the little orphan, right at her heels and crying more pitifully than ever.

Kabato made her decision. She called to Anang and Anoki, who were waiting eagerly to come down from their tree and investigate this unexpected new playmate. At their mother's grunt they fell into line behind her, and now three little cubs followed Kabato northward along the trail. Paji scrambled along behind without a backward look. All the fear and horror of the past two days seemed wiped from her brief young memory, and she knew only that she had found another mother bear to follow and two friendly playmates she had never had.

For more than a mile Kabato kept them moving at a steady pace, till they were well away from the scene of the tragedy. At last, in the early evening, she heeded the cubs' hungry whining and lay down beneath a pine root to let them nurse. Anang and Anoki found their places and sucked eagerly, while Paji hung back, much hungrier than the others but too timid to nurse without an invitation. Kabato grunted softly to the little orphan and opened her arms wide to make room. Joyously Paji ran to her and, side by side with Anoki, drank Kabato's good milk to her heart's content. There were nipples and milk enough for all, and soon Paji's own crooning song of pleasure joined with Anoki's and Anang's.

Kabato nuzzled and licked the little cinnamon cub with her tongue, accepting her as her own, while Paji drank and drank as if she could never get enough. Long after Anoki and Anang had finished and romped off for after-supper games, Paji still nursed in Kabato's arms, and finally she fell asleep, still clinging to Kabato's big warm body. Little Paji was motherless no more. She had found a new family ready-made, even a brother and sister, and in her happiness past grief and terrors were forgotten.

The next day the three cubs had their first real chance to get acquainted. Anoki and Anang were enchanted with their new little sister and promptly showed her all their stunts and tricks. Anoki was delighted to have a new audience to show off to, and she clowned and climbed and somersaulted till she was breathless. At first Paji was so timid she dared only watch and admire her big sister and brother, but soon she lost her shyness and happily joined in their games of tag and hide-and-seek. She found Anang a kind and gentle brother, but it was Anoki she admired most, marveling at her saucy antics and tagging after her in adoration.

While the three cubs rolled and played, Kabato fed hungrily in a poplar thicket. Bending the young saplings to the ground,

she stripped the tops and tender new leaves with her paws and ate great quantities of this good green salad. She set a more leisurely pace today, knowing that Paji must build up her strength and letting the youngsters play and get acquainted. Kabato herself needed plenty of time to feed and hunt for food if she was to provide milk for the extra youngster. More and more she encouraged the cubs to try other foods as well as milk, and gradually they learned to like the new and different flavors.

Day after day the black-bear family wandered happily through the northern woodlands. June had come, bringing the trees and shrubs to full leaf and warm nights as well as days. Yellow bellworts bloomed in the grassy clearings, and the white flowers of Solomon's-seal gleamed in shaded recesses. The glossy partridgeberry leaves covered the forest floor in many places, and its tiny white blooms gave promise of the aromatic red berries to come.

The ruffed grouse, who loved to eat these berries, were courting now, and the bear cubs often watched their colorful theatrical performance. One day a cock ruffed grouse glided in to a big rotten log near where the cubs were playing. They heard a low rumble like a gasoline motor starting in the distance, picking up speed, then stopping suddenly. The cock grouse made this drumming sound by standing on the log, cupping his wings, and clapping them slowly at first, then faster and faster. This was his courting "song," and he repeated it over and over until two female grouse flew to his log, one after another. Then what a show the cock put on to entertain

his ladies! With neck ruff raised and his wide banded tail spread out, he strutted on the log and drummed imperiously. Then suddenly the show was over, and with a loud, whirring roar all three grouse took off, like three rockets from a launching pad, startling the bear cubs with the noise and wind of their wings.

On warm days in early June, Kabato loved to wade into the marshy areas where cowslips were blooming on the mucky bottoms. There she ate the cowslips, flowers, leaves, and all, browsing like a cow on pasture. If the black flies or mosquitoes bothered her, or if the day was hot, she finished off her meal with a cool mud bath. Then the cubs would join her, splashing gaily in the cool, wet muck, rolling and wallowing to their hearts' content.

Each cub made its own little wallow next to Kabato's, and what a sight they made—one big bear and three little ones all grunting and rolling happily with their four feet in the air as they coated their hot, itching bodies with the soothing mud. Kabato purred a deep bass song of bliss as she rolled and rubbed away the patchy remnants of her heavy winter fur, and Anang, Anoki, and Paji added their own purring songs of pleasure as they wriggled and rolled. At last Kabato led them out of the mudbath and into the woods, where they rubbed the excess mud off on the tree-trunks and continued on their travels much refreshed.

13. A Narrow Escape

One day in June, about three weeks after Paji had joined the family, Kabato found a big patch of clover blossoms in a sunny clearing. She ate the sweet blooms eagerly and tried to coax the cubs to try some too. But they were in no mood for new tastes today and raced about the clearing playing a rowdy, noisy game of tag. They dashed between Kabato's legs, under her nose, and round and round her till her patience was worn thin. She wanted to eat in peace and quiet, for food is serious business to a mother bear and it took much time to eat enough to satisfy her hunger.

With a stern cough, Kabato sent the cubs straight up the nearest tree, with the usual understanding that they were to stay there till she told them to come down. Paji obeyed at once, for she would never think of disobeying her kind new foster mother; but Anoki and Anang were more reluctant. They saw no danger threatening, so why must they sit in the tree when they would much rather continue their rambunctious games? Anoki hung back, whining, but one swat from her mother's paw changed her mind. She climbed up with the others and perched on a branch while Kabato went back to the clover patch to feed in peace.

A half-hour passed while the three cubs amused themselves

with acrobatics in the branches. Kabato fed hungrily, making good use of this opportunity and moving gradually farther out of sight of the cubs' big birch tree. Beyond a clump of aspen she found a patch of fresh new bracken shoots, with pale green fronds still furled and tender as asparagus. Time passed quickly as she browsed on the luscious shoots, and though she knew the cubs might get impatient, she also knew that they were safe in the big birch tree.

An hour passed, and the cubs were getting bored. They had used up all their branch-hanging and swinging games and they wanted to come down. Anoki and Anang began to whine, calling peevishly to their mother; but she had wandered out of sight and hearing, busy with her feeding and confident her cubs would wait where they were told to. But it was June, the sunlit woods trails beckoned, and bold Anoki felt she couldn't wait. There was no danger here to keep them up the tree, and anyway she wanted to show Paji how grown-up she was.

With a great sense of daring, disobedient Anoki climbed down the tree and called invitingly to Paji and Anang to join her. Anang was torn between his wish to come down and play and his knowledge that he must obey Kabato; but in the end, naughty Anoki's tempting won him over. Poor Paji didn't dare stay all alone up in the birch tree. Soon all three cubs were on the ground and scampering back along the trail by which they had come.

Anoki led the way, and soon they were all racing merrily, playing hide-and-seek in the underbrush, not realizing how far they were straying from the trail. Each had several turns at

hiding and at seeking, wandering ever farther into the forest, till suddenly they came upon another trail, quite strange and unfamiliar. This was much wider than a deer trail, with two worn, dusty tracks and green grass grown up between, quite different from any trail they'd ever seen. It was an old logging road, still used at times by forest rangers and conservation agents.

Looking up and down this strange wide road, the three young cubs began to feel a little lost and frightened. Anang was calling to his sisters to turn back when they heard a growing rumble. The earth began to shake beneath their feet, and suddenly, around a bend, a great monster approached them at high speed, swirling a cloud of dust. For an instant the cubs crouched in the road, too frightened to move. Then they scrambled in terror for the underbrush—all but little Paji, who was paralyzed by fear.

The truck—for that is what the monster was—ground to a halt, just missing Paji by a hair's breadth. In it were two

conservation officers of the Minnesota Conservation Commission, posted at Grand Marais. They had been out planting trout in some of the many trout streams of the area, and now they were returning on the old logging trail toward the dirt road down the Cascade River and thence to Grand Marais.

As Art, the chief warden, got out of the pick-up truck, Paji tried again to run for cover. But Charlie, the other warden, was already on the other side of her, cutting off her retreat. Not knowing what to do, poor Paji cowered in the road, crying and whining for Kabato.

"Well, what do you know," said Charlie in amazement. "Three little bear cubs out on their own, and their mother nowhere in sight. It's lucky our brakes are good, or we'd have run them over sure."

"We may have hit this little cinnamon cub," Art said concernedly, kneeling down and looking at Paji closely. "It didn't run with the others. Maybe we'd better take it along with us. I'd hate to leave an injured cub with no mother bear to care for it."

Charlie agreed, and in a moment Paji was gently but securely tied in a sack that Art brought from the truck.

"How about the other two cubs?" Charlie asked, looking over to a tamarack stub at the edge of the trail where Anang and Anoki had climbed pell-mell as high as they could go and were clinging and crying for Kabato. "It seems to me their mother would be here by now unless something had happened to her. I wouldn't want to leave them here to starve. They're still too young to make it on their own."

"That's right, Charlie," Art replied. "You know, the department is always on the lookout for orphaned bear cubs for the State Fair exhibit in Saint Paul. We'd better take the black ones along with little Brownie."

The two men got another sack from the truck, an iron bar, and an ax for safety's sake. They walked to the tamarack stub where Anang and Anoki still clung and cried. Charlie climbed to where Anoki sat, some ten feet up on a dead branch. Prying gently with the iron bar, he tumbled her into the sack Art held below. Anang was next, and though he scratched and bit, he soon joined Anoki in the burlap sack. Now their squalling and squealing grew louder than ever as all three frightened cubs called for their mother. How they wished they had obeyed her orders and stayed safely where she had told them!

While Art and Charlie were carrying the two sacks of bear cubs to the truck, Kabato had returned at last to the birch tree where she left her youngsters. Full of good clover and bracken shoots, she was ready to nurse the cubs and then resume their travels. She grunted, calling to the cubs to come down, but not a sound came in reply. Looking up, she saw the tree was empty, with not a cub in sight. Now she was alarmed. Never before had they disobeyed her orders in this way, and she had no idea what could have happened.

Sniffing anxiously around the tree trunk, she caught the scents of all three cubs leading back into the forest and, with her nose close to the ground, she followed their scent along the trail. For a little way the three scents led in one direction, but soon, where the cubs had begun their game of hide-and-seek, the scents led every which way through the underbrush. Poor Kabato did not know which one to follow and ran distracted through the brush, snuffing and grunting in dismay.

Suddenly in the distance she heard a rumble as the truck motor started up. She stopped and listened in alarm, and then, above the distant motor, she heard her youngsters' anguished crying. In the truck Charlie was saying, "Well, I guess the mother bear would surely have showed up by now if she was still around."

"I think so too," Art said. "We'd better get a move on to get back by dark." And he started the truck moving slowly down the rutted logging trail, with Paji, Anoki, and Anang still wailing and bawling in the two sacks on the back of the pick-up.

Back in the forest Kabato heard the motor and her youngsters' cries moving farther and farther away. She whirled in the direction of their calls, and Kabato "the runner" ran as even she had never run before, crashing through the brush and plunging through vines and thickets, racing as fast as her powerful legs would carry her after those heartrending wailings. For a moment she lost the direction of the sounds. She stopped, panting heavily, and then she caught the cries again, a little nearer this time, rising above the grinding noise of the truck in second gear.

In a moment Kabato burst through the brush onto the old logging trail. There her nose and ears told her clearly which way the monster had carried off her cubs. She smelled the man smell also, and though she had learned long ago to fear it, nothing now could keep her from her cubs. In a final burst of speed she galloped down the logging road, and in a few minutes she had almost caught up with the slow-moving truck on the rutted corduroy road.

"Turn around and look behind us, Charlie," Art said in surprise as he glanced in the rear-view mirror. Charlie looked back and saw the big black mother bear racing down the road after the truck.

"Well, we sure guessed wrong that time," Charlie said as Art stopped the truck. "She must have just found out her cubs were missing. These young ones aren't orphans after all, just disobedient cubs. What do we do now?"

"We'd better give them back to her," Art said. "I'd hate to break up a happy family. But I don't think the cinnamon cub is hers, and we still don't know whether it's hurt or not. Let's just give her back her two black cubs and keep little Brownie for the State Fair."

"Be careful," Charlie warned as he got out of the truck. "You know how dangerous a mother bear can be when she thinks her cubs are threatened."

Art took the ax and Charlie a long pole as they came around behind the truck, ready to ward off any danger from the mother bear. But Kabato made no move to attack them. All her attention was focused on the two squirming sacks on the back of the truck. Back and forth she paced uneasily, still panting from her desperate run, and all the time she whined and grunted anxiously to let her youngsters know that she was there. Joyfully they squealed to hear her voice, and when Art cautiously

dumped out the bigger sack, two little black bears ran to Kabato in happy relief. Kabato lost no time in herding them before her into the woods and up a jack pine tree.

"Well, she's got her two cubs back," Charlie said, watching them go. "I think she'll be satisfied and never miss the little brown one."

Both men were just about to get back into the truck and drive off when Kabato appeared again, coming straight toward them. Again she made no threat to attack them but came and sat as close to Paji's sack as she could get, looking from the wardens to the truck and back again, begging them to give her back her adopted cinnamon cub.

"Who says bears can't count?" Art said. "That mother bear wants *all* her youngsters back, and she won't take no for an answer. I guess the fair will have to get along without them."

"She'll do a better job caring for them than we could, Art." And Charlie swung Paji's sack off the truck and turned her out gently into Kabato's eager arms. Paji whimpered with joy all the way into the woods as she and Kabato disappeared for the last time from the wardens' sight and joined Anoki and Anang in safety.

Art and Charlie were thoughtful as they watched them go. "You know, I'm glad those cubs weren't orphans after all," Art said. "They have a brave, wise mother to take care of them, and I'll bet she teaches them never to disobey again. I hope they learned today to stick to bear ways and bear country and not to get too close to man."

"You're right, Art," Charlie said. "Too many bears are

spoiled by garbage dumps and tourists. People shouldn't tempt bears to leave their wild ways or get too tame; it just makes trouble for us all. Bears are born wild and free in their own forest territories, and I think that's how the good Lord wants them to stay."

"Amen," said Art, and the two wardens got into their truck and started slowly back to Grand Marais.

14. Journey to Brule Lake

When Kabato and Paji reached the tree where Anang and Anoki were waiting, Kabato called them down and herded them all before her through the brush. Tired and shaken though they all were, Kabato did not dare to pause or rest till they had gone a mile or more into deep woods. At last she stopped beneath a balsam thicket. Gathering her three weary youngsters round her, she sniffed and nuzzled each one tenderly, so glad that they were safe and unhurt that she could not scold them harshly.

Their frightening experience was punishment enough, and all the cubs felt chastened and far wiser than before. Now they knew what terrible things could happen when they disobeyed. But Kabato held them all close in her arms and licked the fearful man smell off them while they nursed. None of them was hurt or bruised, not even Paji, but they had all learned that man and his monster-trucks are dangerous enemies to be avoided.

They slept that night in the dense balsam thicket, all curled up close together. The experience with the wardens had troubled Kabato deeply. She was determined now to take her cubs to the most isolated spot she knew, where they would be safe from human interference. Her memory told her of a region she had visited in summers past, north of Brule Lake and far from any roads or even logging trails. There she remembered wide, sunny hillsides above the blue lake waters, where forest fires in previous years had burned away the pines and aspens.

On the burned-over slopes blueberry and raspberry bushes now grew in profusion, and in the long grass strawberries would be already ripening. Small streams tumbled down the hillsides to the lake, and rocky points and promontories jutted out along many miles of shoreline. On those windswept points and sunny slopes, Kabato remembered, the summer breezes blew away the pesky black flies and mosquitoes, and there were berries and fish enough for a whole summer's eating.

Kabato knew she must turn west to reach Brule Lake. How far it was she could not tell, but as they traveled she recognized old landmarks—a bear tree by the trail, a high cliff above a stream gorge, or muskeg bogs that were too wet for walking. Mile after mile she led the way through woods and around marshes, over ridges and along game trails, navigating their course westward by following her nose and ears and wise bear instincts.

At times the cubs were hard put to keep up with their mother. They begged for time to rest and play among the windfalls in the spruce bogs or in the fragrant fern beds. But Kabato urged them on. For several days they stopped only long enough to eat and sleep. On warm, still days the deerflies pestered them unmercifully, but Kabato would not let them loll in mudbaths to escape the insects. When they could follow along a stream or lake shore, however, Kabato and cubs alike waded and splashed with delight through the cool water, foiling their insect tormentors.

They traveled for several days, trending always westward but often retracing their steps or detouring north or south as Kabato looked for landmarks to guide her. One day early in July they came out from a jack-pine grove onto a rocky lakeshore. Stretching westward from their vantage point was the longest expanse of water the cubs had ever seen, a large lake stretching farther than the eye could reach. The lake was dotted with rocky, pine-clad islands and bound by long, irregular granite shorelines. In places the tall pines grew right to the rocky edge, but here and there along the shore burnedover hillsides and marshy stream-beds varied the pattern.

This was Brule Lake, Kabato's goal, named long ago by French explorers of the northern wilderness. "Brûlé" is the French word for "burned"; perhaps even then the forests on the lake shore were subject to fires caused by lightning and dry weather. Here at last Kabato knew she would find the quiet slopes she had been seeking, not here at the western end of the lake, but farther along the northern shore.

There were still many rocky points and bays to cross, and now Kabato decided to save time by swimming. Crossing from point to point by water would be much shorter than following the irregular shoreline. The cubs had had no formal swimming lessons, although Anang had had one lesson from the otters; but it was high time they learned.

When Kabato plunged into the water, the cubs were only too glad to follow. It was a hot day, and the cool lake waters were pleasant and inviting. At first Kabato kept to the shallow water near shore, with Anang, Anoki, and Paji splashing happily along behind. Gradually she headed farther out across the bay, and now the cubs could no longer wade but had to swim to follow. Whining in alarm, Anoki and Paji called for Kabato to wait as they splashed awkwardly with all four feet, trying desperately to catch up with their mother. Anang felt quite superior as he paddled on ahead. He was far from a skillful swimmer, but his first lesson with the otters had taught him he could easily stay afloat, and he had no fear of sinking.

Kabato quietly urged the youngsters on, swimming ahead of them but watching carefully to check their progress. Soon all three, even timid Paji, were swimming like old hands, for once they found how buoyant their furry bodies were, they lost their fear and struck out confidently. Kabato slowed her strokes to keep just ahead of the cubs, and when they reached the tip of the first rocky point she let them rest and catch their breath before they struck out across the next small bay.

As they rested on a mossy rock ledge they saw a mother moose coaxing her calf into the water. They too were taking a water shortcut. When the moose calf hesitated at the water's

edge, its mother nudged the baby into the lake. For a moment it sank out of sight but soon bobbed up again, splashing frantically with its long spindly legs. Slowly but surely the baby made its way after the mother moose, much aided by the "life preserver" hairs in its coat, which are hollow and filled with air to help the moose calf stay afloat. Because of these hollow hairs, moose calves can swim easily, while deer fawns cannot, for deer do not have these air-filled hairs to buoy them up.

Kabato kept a watchful eye on the mother moose till she and her calf were out of sight. She had not forgotten that it was a moose that had killed Paji's mother, but she knew also that that had been a tragic accident. Moose and bears, like most large forest creatures, can live in peace together in the wilderness when each respects the other's rights and interests. Kabato took care never to intrude on the privacy of her forest neighbors, and so she was respected but not feared by most north-woods creatures.

Across the third small bay Kabato found the lush and sunny hillside she remembered. Facing southward into the sun, the sand-and-gravel slope was covered with ripe wild strawberries strewn like jewels among the grass and clover. A cool breeze swept the slope, driving away the flies and mosquitoes, and at the edge of the wide clearing two does and their fawns grazed quietly near a sheltering stand of Norways. Pasque-flowers had bloomed here in the spring, and Kabato dug their roots and feasted on them. For dessert she and the cubs scooped strawberries by the pawful into their mouths, reveling in their sweetness and licking the good juice from their muzzles. Grass and clover were mingled with the berries as they ate, and the cubs found the lush greens as good as Kabato had always tried to tell them they were.

As evening approached through the long northern twilight, Kabato called her three tired cubs to follow her to the top of the hill. There she found a hollow beneath a giant granite boulder that had been left here long ago by the glacial ice sheets that once covered this land. Settling herself under the sheltering rock, Kabato opened her arms for the youngsters to come and nurse. Tired but happy after their long journey, the cubs suckled sleepily while a great yellow moon rose slowly over the opposite shore.

On the slope below them the shadowy forms of several does grazed peacefully in the dusk, while their fawns gamboled in circles, jumping stiff-legged. From the pine grove a whippoorwill called over and over his sweet, monotonous song. Far down on the shore of the lake the mother moose appeared with her calf, drinking and wading in the shallow water. Beavers and muskrats worked and fed in the last little bay the bears had crossed, and all along the lake shore Nature welcomed the warm summer night.

Kabato and the cubs curled, sleepy and content, in the hollow beneath the boulder. The night breeze brought the sweet smell of strawberries up the slope, and the scent of fresh water and pine. Just before Kabato drifted off to sleep she heard the liquid music of the hermit thrush singing its lullaby from deep among the pines. Filled with contentment, she knew she had found for her cubs a black bear's summer paradise.

15. The Peaceable Kingdom

In the sunny days that followed, the bears feasted on strawberries till every plant was stripped. To vary their diet they
browsed on grass and clover, and often they added a taste of
ants as a tart salad dressing. When Kabato found an anthill
in the clearing she called the cubs and tore the hill apart.
Hordes of angry ants rushed out, some carrying eggs from the
ant nursery. Kabato and the cubs thrust their forepaws into
the nest, then licked off the ants that swarmed over their fur.
The ants and eggs alike had a sharp tang that tasted good when
the sweetness of berries had begun to pall.

Kabato never tired of exploring the hillsides and the nearby
streams and bays, looking for good things to eat. But Paji,
Anoki, and Anang would rather play than eat. The open

hillside was a perfect playground, and they loved to roll like balls from top to bottom. One after another they rolled into the cool lake water at the foot of the slope, squealing and splashing and turning water somersaults. Then back again to the top of the hill they raced to start all over.

The first day they played this game Anang was leading the way up the hill when he noticed a quick movement across the slope. Alert and curious, he angled over to investigate, Anoki and Paji following close behind. As they approached they saw a large hole in the hillside and peering from it four little heads with pointed ears and noses. Four red fox kits lived here with their mother in a den she had enlarged from an old badger digging. Round the door of the den lay remains of mice and rabbits and other food the parent foxes had brought to feed their offspring. Though the odor of decaying meat was strong, the foxes' own scent was powerful too, and they didn't seem to mind such careless housekeeping.

Anang sniffed mightily at these interesting new smells, and Anoki and Paji crept close to investigate. The four little foxes were just as curious as the bear cubs were, and soon there was much two-way sniffing and friendly whining. Anoki ran about in circles and boxed and wrestled with Anang and Paji, clowning and trying to coax the fox kits to come out and join them.

Impy, the biggest of the fox cubs, could not resist the invitation. Crawling cautiously, with his body close to the ground, he wriggled closer and closer to the bear cubs, whining a peculiar, enticing call to the cubs, who watched him in amazement. He was nearly within reach of Anoki when he leaped suddenly into the air. With one jump he flew right over her head and landed on the other side, leaving her gaping and dumfounded. Like a jack-in-the-box he leaped around and over the little bears, teasing them with his unpredictable tricks and seeming to laugh at their confusion and surprise.

Now Impy raced about in circles, traveling like a whirlwind, still whining his impish invitation for them to try to catch him. Delightedly Anang took up the challenge and lumbered after Impy as fast as he could go. But somehow he was never fast enough. Impy would lie down coaxingly just out of reach, all four legs spraddled out along the ground. As Anang approached, Impy crawled slowly toward him, feinting and

teasing. At the last moment, when Anang had almost caught him, Impy leaped straight up in the air, floating like thistledown over Anang's head, and off he raced again, with Anang left far behind.

Soon the other little foxes joined the fun. Paji and Anoki took their turns at trying to tag their playmates, but somehow the fox kits were always too quick for them. The cubs were twice as big as their furry red playmates, but the young foxes were far more agile. The foxes always won at games of tag, but when it came to wrestling, the bears outmatched them. When Impy pounced on Paji she gave him a bear hug that made him yip, and then the whole crew piled on them both.

A furry mass of red and brown and black tumbled and squealed all up and down the hillside, till finally Anoki rolled with Impy right to the water's edge.

At the last moment Impy pulled free and sat panting on the shore while Anoki tried to coax him into the cool blue lake. Anang and Paji put their heads between their legs and rolled down into the water too; but all their coaxing couldn't tempt the fox kits even to get their feet wet. For a time they watched from shore while the three bears dived and splashed in the hot summer afternoon, but soon their vixen mother called them back to the den for dinner.

As evening approached, Kabato called the cubs to the bank of the stream where she was fishing. Where the stream flowed into the lake Kabato had found a school of suckers, and now she flipped them from the shallow stream-mouth out onto the shore. Some of the fish flopped back into the water and escaped; others she pounced on and seized firmly in her teeth. By the time the cubs arrived she had caught more than enough for their supper.

Their long afternoon of games with their new fox playmates had given the cubs a hearty appetite. They tore open the fish with relish and ate till they were bursting; but even then more fish lay temptingly on shore where Kabato had left them. The bears were not the only hungry ones that evening. From a distance a family of ravens smelled the fish and flew upwind, calling and croaking to others to join the feast. Perching in the pines, they kept up a noisy clamor as they watched and waited impatiently for the bears to finish their supper.

The ravens' croaking attracted other animals. A beautiful cross fox with shoulder bands of black among his red fur lurked silently at the edge of the pines. This was Chinook, the father of the fox kits, who lived in a rock den in the woods and stood guard and hunted food for his family in the hillside burrow. The young fox kits' appetites kept Chinook and his vixen busy, and now he hoped to share in the plentiful supply of suckers Kabato had caught.

Crawling on his belly, just as Impy had that afternoon, Chinook cautiously approached the spot where the mother bear was still feasting on the fish. Kabato ignored him, for the cubs had finished eating and there were still fish aplenty. Quick as a flash Chinook seized a large sucker in his teeth and bounded away to the hillside den with his prize. His success emboldened the ravens, and they circled nearer, soaring above Kabato but never quite daring to land. Just as one raven gathered up his courage, Chinook returned and with a snarl drove off the big black bird. Neither bears nor foxes liked the ravens, for they sometimes attacked defenseless kits and cubs. Now Chinook felt that he and this mother bear were friends and allies, and with no more ado he fetched and carried suckers up the hillside to his family till they too had more than they could eat.

Kabato paid no attention, eating her supper placidly till even she could hold no more. In a leisurely way she licked her chops and paws and, calling to the cubs, moved up the lake shore for an evening bath. The ravens waited restlessly for her departure, but no sooner had Kabato and Chinook left the sucker banquet than a coyote, or brush wolf, crept out of the shadows to take over. With his thick, creamy gray fur and bushy tail he looked bigger than he really was, and again the ravens feared to come too close. If they approached he growled and jumped at them. After his first hunger was appeased, he raised his head and wailed his feed call. The mournful howl echoed across the still lake waters, and soon from the pines came his mate's reply. Now both coyotes crouched and ate their fill of the remaining suckers and carried away in their mouths enough to feed their young ones in their nearby den in the cliffs.

Only then, as sunset reddened the evening sky and all the other larger creatures had had their share, did the ravens dare to finish up the feast. They gobbled hastily as darkness fell, and when at last they flew away to roost along the rocky cliffs, only a few scraps and scales remained. During the summer night even those remnants disappeared as shrews and mice and even a barred owl silently devoured the last fishy morsels. Thus Kabato's afternoon of fishing had fed not only her own cubs but many other woodland families in their northern paradise.

One lovely summer day followed another in this peaceable kingdom. All the many north-woods creatures seemed to live in perfect harmony with each other, as Isaiah prophesied in the Bible of the animals on the New Earth. Bears, deer, foxes, moose, and coyotes ranged and fed over the hillsides and along the lake shore, while ruffed and spruce grouse shared the lush wild strawberries. The young grouse were half-grown and old enough to fly, and already the young cocks practiced their drumming and strutting and challenged one another in mock duels.

The downy woodcock chicks who lived along the boggy bays were already as big as their parents, and young and old put on a comic show each day as they probed along the muddy shores with their long bills. They thrust their bills into the mud full length and cupped their wings and thrashed the ground to attract unwary angleworms.

The bear cubs, swimming on hot afternoons, watched the woodcocks and sandpipers along the shore while over the water errant bands of herring gulls swooped playfully about their heads, calling their shrill cries before they moved on to other waters. At dusk the wild and haunting music of the loons echoed from bay to bay and point to point across the lake; and as the bears drifted off to sleep in their hollow on the hillside, the whole northern wilderness seemed to sing them into slumber.

16. The End of Summer

In early August the blueberries ripened in the old burned clearings. High on the hilltop Kabato and the cubs scooped the luscious dark berries into their mouths by the pawful, blowing out the leaves and stems. When the blueberries were gone, raspberries took their place. The raspberry canes grew thick along the edges of the woods, and brambly blackberries waited to ripen when the red raspberries were gone. Berries of every kind, plenty of fish, and mud wallows to luxuriate in on hot days kept Kabato and the cubs content day after day.

Their fox kit playmates were a constant delight to the bear cubs. Each day they met and played their familiar games all up and down the hillside. While Anang, Anoki, and Paji did their barrel rolls down the slope. Impy and his sisters ran

130

circles round the cubs, leapfrogged over them, and tried to block their rolling by throwing themselves in the cubs' downhill path. The sturdy young bears were so big that the slender fox kits seldom won at this contest, and more than once Anang came barreling down the hill so fast he pulled Impy right along with him into the water at the bottom.

Crestfallen Impy didn't like to get wet, and when he was outfoxed this way he challenged Anang to another kind of game. Leaping gracefully onto a high, round boulder, Impy and the other fox kits dared the plump young cubs to come up too. The cubs ran round and round the rock, looking for a foothold so they could climb up. But there was no foothold, and their roly-poly bodies couldn't make it up the smooth, steep rock. Instead Anoki raced to the nearest pine tree and, with Paji and Anang close behind, she climbed till they were all high above the little foxes on their boulder. There they squealed in glee, while the fox kits yapped and barked right back as if to say, "No one won this time. Let's call it a draw."

In August the foxes moved to a new den higher up the hillside. That is how the vixen fox "cleaned house"; when the old den got too dirty she simply moved her family to a clean new burrow. While the vixen rested in her sunny doorway, father Chinook went hunting mice with all his kits and the three bear cubs tagging along. As Chinook ranged over the hillside he would sniff, stop, listen, then jump with both forefeet and dig quickly, and usually he came up with a mouse or a whole nest of mice.

The young bears liked to eat mice too, but their technique

for hunting them was not as expert as the foxes'. Impy soon learned to imitate his father, jumping stiff-legged on many a mouse nest that the bears had missed. Sometimes when Impy caught a mouse he brought it to Paji or Anoki and let it fall before them. When Paji pounced to pick it up, Impy was one jump quicker and snatched the mouse away from under her nose. Then he would run in circles, stop, and hold the mouse with his forepaws, tempting the bear cubs to take it from him.

When Paji rose to the challenge Impy growled and threatened to bite her nose, but Paji had learned not to fear his playful warnings. She growled right back, knocked Impy's paw away, and covered the mouse with her own broad paw. Then Impy cried as if his heart were breaking, dug fast beneath her paw, and, before she could stop him, snatched the mouse and raced away with all the little bears and foxes in pursuit. This game of "Mouse, mouse, who's got the mouse?" was played again and again with many variations, sometimes with a frog or

sucker; and everyone thought it was great fun, except the poor mouse or frog who was the victim.

Toward the end of August, when the nights were growing cooler and many birds began to flock for travel, another mother bear and her three cubs came to the north shore of Brule Lake to join the feast of berries. Blackberries and dewberries were ripening at last, and the plentiful crop provided enough for all to share. Kabato kept her distance from the other mother bear, each respecting the other's privacy; but the two mothers allowed their cubs to frolic together without restraint.

Anang, Anoki, and Paji were overjoyed at the visit of the three new bear cubs. They soon introduced them to all their games, from rolling down the hillside to tag and hide-and-seek and many tree-climbing and water games. The new cubs loved to box and wrestle, and the biggest of them was always challenging Anang. Anang had inherited from his father both a big frame and a gentle disposition, so, though he always won the wrestling matches, he was careful not to play too roughly and never hurt his playmates.

All the cubs had grown big and strong during the summer. Even little Paji was plump and husky now, and her sleek red-brown fur made a pretty contrast with Anoki's glossy black coat. Anang, with his star-shaped white mark on his chest, and sturdy black body, was growing up to be a handsome fellow and the apple of Kabato's eye. More and more he reminded her of Koda, and although neither Anang nor Anoki bore Koda's brown-headed markings, Kabato could see Koda's playful spirit in Anoki and in Anang his friendliness and strength.

As the nights grew cooler and September brought the threat of frost, the bears ate eagerly, preparing for the winter to come. The mother bears and cubs alike fed hungrily on all the good foods the northern wilderness provided. Fish in the lake and streams, honey in scattered bee trees, but most of all, berries, fruit, and acorns fattened their bodies in preparation for cold weather and their long winter sleep. Pincherries and choke-cherries hung from the trees in clusters, and on the ridges scrub oaks bore their acorns for many north-woods creatures to enjoy.

The bears climbed out on the cherry and oak limbs, feeding on the luscious fruit and acorns. Often a branch would break beneath their weight, and they clawed wildly to hang on, stripping the leaves and fruit, which fell to the ground for deer and grouse to feast on later. Sometimes Kabato or one of the cubs tumbled to the ground as a branch broke, but they were never hurt and climbed right back to continue their banquet.

Late in September, when the first frosts came, the trees were already glowing with fall color. The birch leaves were the first to turn, their yellow tones blending with the gold of the aspens, shining bright in the autumn sun against the brilliant blue of lake and sky and the dark green masses of the conifers. The reds of the maples flamed along the hillsides, and slowly the oaks took on a bronzed mahogany hue. Mountain-ash berries gleamed in scarlet clusters against the white birch trunks, and all the north woods seemed aflame with color.

Many of the migrant birds had left the north country with the first full moon of autumn, flying to their winter homes in

the south. Ducks and geese still landed at sunset on the wide blue waters, but in a day or two each flock was gone, winging its way southward with the sun.

The buck deer on the hillsides prepared for the mating season, rubbing the velvet from their horns on small trees and bushes. The trees used as rubbing posts soon had their bark skinned off. Supple saplings were twisted in the prongs of the buck's antlers as the male deer pawed the ground, tossed his head, and strained and lifted, using all the power in his fast-swelling neck. Charging in regal splendor through the woods and fighting mock battles with shrubs and saplings, the bucks made preparation for the real battles of the mating season, when each buck would strive to gather many does into his harem.

Early in October the other family of bears left Brule Lake, moving on to look for winter quarters. The blackberries were gone, and many trees were bare, but Kabato still lingered in their summer paradise, catching fish for the cubs and feasting on acorns and roots. The cubs ate eagerly of all the foods Kabato found for them, and more and more they enjoyed hunting and fishing for themselves. They were so busy finding food they did not have much time to play with their old play-mates the fox kits, but now and then, for old times' sake, the seven youngsters boxed and raced and rolled as they had all summer, enjoying their last childhood games together. Soon the fox kits would be full-grown adults, busy with hunting and raising families; and soon the bear cubs would have to leave this peaceful hillside.

The days grew shorter, and the nights grew colder. Kabato and the cubs had all grown fat and roly-poly with their eager feeding, and the chill air did not penetrate their long, thick fur. But the hollow beneath the boulder where they slept was not a proper winter shelter, and Kabato at last made plans to leave Brule Lake. When the ice formed a thin skin around the lake shore and did not melt entirely in the sun, when all the summer birds were gone and chipmunks disappeared into their burrows, and when the first snow coated the bare berry canes and browned hillside grass—then Kabato called the cubs with a soft growl and led the way south from their peaceable kingdom.

The biggest and the best winter den Kabato knew was the old giant pine on the ridge where they had spent the early spring. There was room in the hollow tree for all the family, a bigger family now with Paji added and with each cub at least four times as big as it had been when they left in the spring. Kabato did not know how far they must travel to find the ridge once more, but she knew the general direction they must go. Day by day, and often by nighttime too, under the brilliant stars of Orion and the Pleiades and the bright glow of autumn

northern lights, Kabato traced their way patiently back along the route they had followed in early summer.

Often she took shortcuts, sniffing and sensing in instinctive ways which trail or stream to follow. Now the cubs could follow and match her pace with far less effort than in the spring, but they still insisted on time out for fun and games along the way. As the days grew colder, the bears' appetites gradually decreased, their stomachs shrank, and they stopped less often to eat and oftener to sleep.

The first real snowfall in early November found them near the pool in the stream where the otters had fished for lampreys. Here the bears stayed for several days in the rock den where they had slept the previous spring. The cubs were so sleepy now they would have been happy to spend the winter curled up right there, crowded though they were; but Kabato roused them and led them on, knowing the pine ridge above the cedar swamp could not be far away. Next day they reached the bear tree at the end of the ridge, and after Kabato had left her marks upon it she pressed on determinedly along the old familiar trail.

Anoki and Paji were so sleepy they could hardly stumble along the trail, and drowsy Anang longed to curl up under each balsam thicket that they passed. Kabato too was drowsy, but she urged the youngsters on, nudging Anang sharply when he lay down for a nap, and nipping Anoki and Paji into wakefulness. At last, at twilight on a gray November afternoon, they came through the grove of Norways to the old white pine they had known so well long months ago. Anang and Anoki dimly

remembered their old home in the hollow tree, and to all three sleepy cubs its sturdy hollow trunk was a longed-for haven. Drowsily they helped Kabato carry in dead leaves and soft pine needles to line the sawdust floor. Then, without a murmur, the three cubs curled up in the darkness and fell fast asleep.

Sleepily Kabato crawled in after them and with a deep and happy sigh stretched out across the entrance. Just before she drifted into slumber she heard an old familiar sound. "Hoo, hoo-hoo, hoo, hoo," came the eerie five-note call of Bubo, the great horned owl, still standing guard over the giant pine and seeming to welcome the bears back home once more. Kabato was content. Her family was safe and snug for the long winter, and now she too could sink into the sleep she longed for.

17. A New Year—and a Meeting

All winter long Kabato and the three cubs slept or dozed in the hollow pine. The cubs were no longer nursing, and this winter, like Kabato, they went without food and water. The thick layer of fat they had built up during the fall, and their long, heavy fur, kept them warm even when the outdoor temperature dropped to forty below. Snowdrifts piled high around the tree and over the entrance to their den, adding a thick layer of insulation against the cold. Fresh air and a few snowflakes sifted into the den from knotholes in the trunk above, and the bears' nest stayed clean and odorless through the long winter months.

This was a winter of heavy snows. In the cedar swamp below the ridge many deer gathered to make a winter yard and feeding ground. Their trails criss-crossed the swamp in all directions, and after each snowfall the deer tramped down the trails again to keep them passable. Cedar and spruce boughs were their chief foods, as the deep snows covered most other greens and bushes. Timber wolves prowled the region, chasing weakened and hungry deer along the trails in hopes of pulling one down.

The snowshoe rabbits had reached a population peak this winter, and their large numbers affected the whole game cycle of the northern woods. The previous winter snowshoe rabbits had reached their peak farther north in Canada, but this year many meat-eating birds and animals moved south to Minnesota, where the rabbits were now abundant. Large white snowy owls came down from the Arctic north into the Superior wilderness, seeking to feed on them. Goshawks with fierce beaks and pearly breasts came too, along with many foxes, wolves, lynx, weasels, fishers, and even a pair of rare wolverines wandering far from their Canadian home.

A weasel chasing a snowshoe rabbit pursued his quarry relentlessly, over and under the snow, beneath the brush and over fallen trees, never stopping or turning aside until at last the wearied rabbit could run no longer and fell prey to the hunter weasel. But the rabbit's shrill cry as the weasel seized him attracted other animals, and both hunter and hunted became food for a pair of foxes. When they had eaten their fill, two Canada jays, or "whisky-jacks," flew down to finish the remains. Thus the abundant snowshoe rabbits, against their will, provided sustenance for many of their wilderness neighbors.

Kabato and the three cubs drowsed and slept, unaware of the many forest dramas going on outside their den. When April came with its warmer days and melting snows, the cubs stirred restlessly in the hollow pine; but this year they were not quite so eager to romp and play as they had been when they were babies. Anang was the first to wake and stretch and scratch about, but when he tried to interest Anoki and Paji in a boxing match, they sleepily ignored him.

The days grew warmer, and the sounds of spring grew more inviting. Anoki and Paji woke up one day and found Anang just crawling out the entrance. Yawning and stretching, they followed after, leaving Kabato still snoring peacefully in the nest. Outside, the air was soft and balmy, and the brown pine needles lay bright in the sunlight on the ridgetop trail. Sud-

denly the joy of spring seemed overwhelming. The three young bears rolled and frolicked in the fragrant, spongy needles, wrestling and racing along the ridge with all the pent-up zest of the long winter.

Soon Kabato too emerged from the hollow pine, blinking sleepily in the sunlight. Drowsily she watched the youngsters romping in the sun. Then with a low grunt she called them to follow as she plodded off down the trail to look for water. Snowdrifts still lay unmelted beneath the balsams, and near one thicket a little stream flowed down the ridge. The sound of trickling water made the cubs realize how thirsty they were after the long months without food or drink. Crouching at the spring, the four bears drank long and eagerly till their stomachs could hold no more.

Now Kabato went back to the giant pine for another snooze, but sleep was out of the question for Anang, Anoki, and Paji. They raced and romped all up and down the ridge, climbing the outside trunk of their hollow pine and playing tag with the inquisitive red squirrels and chickadees who frequented its branches. When they grew tired they joined Kabato in the den for a nap, but now that spring was here they hated to waste time in sleep.

As the youngsters played in and around the hollow pine, they grew hungrier and hungrier. Now and then they nibbled at the bark and roots to satisfy their craving for food, but they dared not go to look for a real meal without Kabato's permission. Anoki nudged her mother impatiently, and Anang tickled her ears as she slept, both trying to rouse her to help them find a proper breakfast. Paji added her plaintive, hungry whines, and at last Kabato, with mighty yawns and sleepy groans, decided it really was time to get up.

Leaving the den on a cool but sunny April day, Kabato led the way down the ridge toward the Cascade River. All the bears were sleek-furred and plump, just as when they had gone to sleep in November, but the cubs were bigger by far than when they had left the same den a year ago. Anoki and Paji were about the same size, each weighing about one hundred and twenty-five pounds, nearly half as big as Kabato. Anoki's black fur and Paji's cinnamon coat were glossy in the sunlight, and the white star mark on Anang's chest gleamed bright against his heavy black coat. Anang was growing big, like his father, and already weighed one hundred and fifty pounds.

The cubs would not reach their full growth and weight until they were four or five years old, but even as yearlings they were bigger and stronger than most other north-woods creatures.

Kabato led the cubs first to a balsam thicket. There they chewed on the pungent tips of the branches and the fibrous roots, savoring the resinous juices as a spring tonic after their long fast. After this spring tune-up for their digestive systems, the bears were hungrier than ever. The cubs followed Kabato down into the cedar swamp and feasted on fresh skunk cabbage and roots of water plants. When the youngsters had eaten all they wanted, Anang and Anoki took Paji to the den beneath the fallen cedar where they were born. They probably did not remember those first days of their lives, or even the rising waters that had driven them from their home, but the big fallen cedar was still a fine place to play, and they raced up and down its slanting trunk in high spirits.

They slept that night in the hollow beneath its roots, in the old den they had been born in. The next day Kabato moved on toward the Cascade River. The deer had left their winter yard in the swamp to move to higher ground, but their trails were still plain through the marshy thickets. Feeding on pond-lily roots and other tubers, Kabato approached the rocky cliffs where the swamp, the river, and the pine ridge met.

Once again the Cascade River was roaring with the spring run-off through its rocky gorge. Below the north-facing bank, just above the water level, a deep snowdrift still covered a rocky ledge. As Kabato stopped to drink at the edge of the water, she caught the scent of meat nearby. The cubs sniffed too, for they were eager now for any new addition to their diet. Kabato followed the scent to the deep snowdrift beneath the cliff, and, digging quickly, she soon uncovered the carcass of a deer. During the winter a pack of wolves had chased a herd of deer along the ridgetop trail, and this poor doe had broken its neck in a fall from the top of the cliff. The wolves chased on, still following the others in the herd, and the drifting snow had covered and preserved the deer's carcass.

Black bears seldom kill a deer or any animal so large and swift, but they enjoy meat upon occasion to vary their vegetable diet. Kabato and the cubs gorged on their find, and soon the smell of food brought all the usual onlookers. Crows and ravens flapped into the pines to await their turn at the feast, and Canada jays and even chickadees flew close to steal a few tidbits. The bears allowed these birds to help themselves, but when the ravens tried to approach, Anang and Anoki growled and swatted at them till they flew away. Perhaps they remembered the ravens' attack when they were helpless babies; at any rate, they felt the ravens were not their friends.

When they had eaten all they could, Kabato led the cubs to the nearby den in the ledge where, a year ago, she had intended to move her babies. While the cubs lay down to sleep under the rocky overhang, Kabato stretched out near the half-eaten deer carcass to guard against marauders. It was lucky she did, for soon two timber wolves approached. Drawn by the ravens' calls and the smell of meat, the wolves determined to steal the carcass from Kabato, thinking perhaps that they were entitled to it, as part of the pack that had hunted the deer last winter.

The wolves' strategy was for one of them to distract Kabato while the other seized the carcass. With an angry growl Kabato charged the big male wolf, but he leaped nimbly aside before she could strike him with her powerful paws. The growls and snarls of battle roused the sleeping cubs, and Anang rushed out to join in the fight, with Anoki and Paji close behind. Anang was about to charge the male wolf, who was close to Anang's size, though not as heavy. Just in time Kabato turned and saw Anang's intention. With a stern grunt she ordered him and his sisters up the nearest tree and gave him a hearty swat to speed his progress.

Anang obeyed, but he was much chagrined. From the top of the nearest pine he and Anoki and Paji watched the contest below, and all the while Anang was sure he could have driven away those wolves all by himself. But Kabato knew best. Big though Anang had grown, neither he nor his sisters had judgment enough to tackle so crafty an adversary as a timber wolf; and Kabato had all she could do to protect their food supply from the wolves without having to guard the cubs from their own folly.

While Kabato's attention was distracted, the she-wolf seized the carcass and began to drag it away. When Kabato whirled to attack her, she dodged out of reach, leading Kabato away from the carcass while the male wolf crept in to tear off a chunk of meat. This strategy was repeated many times, and poor Kabato grew more and more tired, frustrated, and angry as she tried to have the food she had found for her family.

She was nearly ready to give up the battle when a deep, rumbling growl came from the end of the rocky ledge. There stood Koda, her mate, his massive body raised to full height as he turned his huge brown head from side to side to see what the commotion was all about. Then he caught Kabato's scent, and he waited no longer. With a growl that seemed to shake the rocky bank and drown out even the roar of the river, Koda rushed into the battle. While Kabato charged the she-wolf, Koda tore after the male, catching him from behind with a mighty blow of his forepaw and sending him fifteen feet through the air. The wolf lit running, and, howling with pain and disappointment, he loped off through the pines as fast as he could travel. His mate lost no time in following, for two black bears were one too many for a pair of wolves to challenge.

When the wolves had gone, Koda approached Kabato hesitantly. He was full of joy at meeting his mate once more, but he knew she might not want him near while their cubs were with her. Tentatively he nudged her muzzle with his nose, snuffing gently, and when Kabato did not snap at him, his happiness was complete. He ran back and forth like a playful puppy along the rocky ledge, then strutted to the nearest aspen and stretched up tall against it. Measuring out his full height on the tree, he proudly clawed and bit the bark to make his mark, the mark of Koda, Kabato's mate, the biggest black bear in the Superior forest.

All this time Anang, Anoki, and Paji watched excitedly from their pine-tree perch. Anang was beside himself with joy at seeing again the wonderful stranger he admired so much. Koda had conquered the wolves, just as Anang had dreamed of doing, and the cub wanted more than anything in the world to climb down the tree and meet him. He couldn't help whining pleadingly to Kabato, begging her to let him come down, and Anoki and Paji joined in the plantive chorus.

For a moment Kabato hesitated. She loved her cubs and her big brown-headed mate, but it was not bear custom that they should meet or live together. Male black bears are sometimes harsh and jealous fathers, but Kabato was sure that Koda, always so gentle and friendly, would love their cubs as she did. With a soft grunt she called the yearlings down from the tree and with a proud and happy heart led them to meet their father.

Big Koda nosed and sniffed each cub in turn—first Anoki, who was so awed by this great stranger she stood quite meek and still; then Paji, the shy adopted one, whose red-brown fur perhaps bespoke some distant kinship with brown-headed Koda; and last Anang, who wriggled all over with happiness and excitement. Koda's own joy knew no bounds, for he understood that these were his children, already grown big and strong in their second year and nearly ready to make their own way in the wilderness.

Anang he inspected with special care. With a playful gesture he put out his paw to the cub, and frisky Anang responded with delight. In an instant they were rolling and tumbling like two cubs together, and with happy squeals Anoki and Paji joined in. Now the banks echoed with their playful growls and grunts as father and cubs wrestled and raced along the rocky ledge, while Kabato stood guard, watching fondly but anxiously over this joyous family meeting.

18. Parting of the Ways

As the spring twilight fell, the tired but happy black-bear family drew apart once more. The cubs were winded from their strenuous play, and even Koda was ready for rest and quiet. While Kabato stood guard, the cubs nibbled at the deer carcass and then curled up for the night in the rocky den under the bank.

Koda withdrew to the far end of the ledge, and only when the cubs were fast asleep did Kabato approach. For a long moment the two bears stood quietly in the April evening while a three-quarter moon rose silently in the eastern sky. They did not need the power of speech to know each other's thoughts and feelings, or to express their deep peace and contentment. They both knew, too, that change was coming for all of them, for soon the cubs would start an independent life. Koda must leave his family now and go his way alone, but he would not be very far away. The mating moon was coming, and he and Kabato would meet again; but now he stood for one last moment by her side, then like a shadow vanished in the night.

In the morning all trace of Koda's visit had disappeared. The disappointed cubs searched every nook and cranny of the rocky ledge, hoping to find a clue to their big father's whereabouts. But even his giant flat pawprints in the snow had melted in the morning sun, and the south wind blew away his scent. When they had finished the last scraps of deer meat, Kabato called the cubs to follow up the river. Anang hung back, his thoughts still full of Koda and a new longing to travel with his father. He was slow to answer Kabato's call, and when she whacked him soundly for his dawdling he sulked and brooded and longed still more to run away with Koda.

As April turned to May and summer's warmth crept northward, the cubs grew more aware of change in Kabato. More and more she encouraged them to forage for food on their own, and she sometimes left them by themselves for hours at a time. When she found an anthill or a nest of grubs, the cubs still came running, expecting to share in the feast. But now Kabato cuffed them away brusquely, telling them plainly that they must look for ants and grubs for themselves. She loved her youngsters as much as ever, but her discipline was far stricter than it had ever been before. She had to prepare them for an independent life of their own, and perhaps she knew that her seeming bad temper would make the parting easier to bear.

Day by day the young bears grew more skillful at finding insects, digging roots, and catching fish for themselves. They had watched Kabato's methods for so long they knew just how things should be done, and with increasing practice each cub grew more and more adept at all the black-bear skills. They traveled over many of the trails they had explored last year, and now each landmark had become familiar. As spring grew into summer, the cubs felt a growing wanderlust, rebellion against Kabato's discipline, and an exciting yearning to strike out on their own.

Early in June a late freeze struck the north woods. The cold snap caught the cherry trees in bloom and froze the berry blossoms. At first the effect on the wilderness food supply was not apparent, for it would be many weeks before the first berries were due to ripen. But dry weather too, in April and May, had reduced the lush growth of cowslips and cinnamon ferns. The bears had to travel farther and search with much diligence to find all the food they needed.

Still, there were plenty of suckers and northern pike in the streams, and bearberries were uncovered by the melting snows. Kabato and the cubs caught fish, ate leaves and clover, bracken and roots, and dug for mice and shrews; and because the cubs had learned their lessons well, they did not go hungry. Sometimes Kabato and the cubs passed other bear families traveling southeastward, heading for the garbage dumps at Lutsen and Tofte on Lake Superior's northwest shore. There they would scavenge for food among tin cans and garbage of man's civilization, while tourists came from miles around to watch and feed and tease them.

Kabato knew the folly of such behavior, for man would sooner or later betray the bears who approached him; and over and over she tried to impress this lesson on the cubs. She remembered well that years ago man had killed her firstborn cub, and two men had nearly stolen her three cubs from her just last summer. By every means she could, she tried to remind Anang, Anoki, and Paji of that near-disaster. Whenever they came to a logging trail or an old trapper's cabin, wherever the scent of man was present, however faint, Kabato gave her warning grunt and turned or drove the cubs away, allowing no curious explorations and heading her family deeper into the wilderness, where few men ever ventured.

One day in July the cubs were fishing in the little lake where they had first seen Koda in the distance, over a year ago. Anoki and Paji were intent on ambushing a crafty pike, while Anang searched along the water's edge for frogs and crayfish. They did not notice that Kabato had disappeared until it was nearly sundown. They waited by the lake shore, watching and calling now and then, but they were half-grown bears by now, no longer frightened at being left alone.

It was nearly dark when silently, without a warning sound, Kabato appeared again beside the lake shore. Koda was with her, a giant black shadow among the pine trees, and Kabato's manner was strange and distant. When Anang saw Koda he started toward him with a squeal of joy, but a deep growl from Kabato stopped him in his tracks. With a low grunt Kabato

ordered the three cubs to climb the nearest tree, and, though
they felt resentful and rebellious, something in Kabato's tone
warned them they must not disobey. When all three cubs had
reached safe perches, Kabato took a long last look and raised
her muzzle toward the three young ones she had loved and
cherished. Then, as silently as they had come, Kabato and
Koda disappeared into the forest.

All that night and part of the next day the cubs waited restlessly in the pine tree for their mother to return. But Kabato
never came. It was the mating season and time for Kabato and
the cubs to part. Next morning, when Anang at last climbed
down, he doggedly set out to follow Kabato and his idol Koda.
But they were already far away, deep in the forests and
traveling fast and free. July had come, the mating moon, and
it was time for yearling cubs to strike out on their own.

When Anang set off to follow Kabato's and Koda's trail,
Anoki and Paji decided they too were free to come down. For
the first few days they reveled in their freedom, fishing for pike
and suckers and roaming wherever they chose. No stern
Kabato cuffed them or imposed her will, and the taste of independence seemed sweet even to docile Paji. The two sisters
missed their brother's comradeship, but Anang too was tasting
the joys of independence as he traveled farther and farther on
his own in search of Koda.

For more than a week Anoki and Paji fished and hunted
food within a few miles of the place Kabato left them. Soon
they had eaten all the roots and grubs available, and fish grew
harder to catch as hot weather drove them to deep waters.
More and more often Anoki and Paji went to sleep still hungry,
and they longed now for Kabato's help in finding food. But
Kabato had her own life to lead with Koda, and before many
months passed she would have new cubs to care for.

Late in July, when the deerflies were especially bothersome
and Anoki and Paji were hot and irritable, Anoki remembered
the cool breezes and lush berries of their summer paradise at

Brule Lake. It took them several days to trace out the way, and they made many wrong turns and followed many strange trails. But they headed always northwest, and at last they came to the wide blue waters and open hillsides they remembered with such pleasure. But all was changed. The late frost and dry weather had killed the berry crop. Where once the strawberries and blueberries had carpeted the ground, there were only green leaves and blasted buds; and the raspberries and blackberries gave promise of only a few blighted berries to come.

Disconsolate and hungry, the two sisters wandered northward into new territory, seeking new berry patches and cold, shallow streams where fish might still be caught. Anoki grew more irritable each day and often snapped at Paji for no reason at all. When she found an anthill or a grub's nest in a rotten log, she would not share these treasures with Paji as she used to, but kept each precious morsel for herself. In self-defense Paji grew far more skillful than Anoki at catching mice and shrews, and generously she almost always caught an extra one for Anoki.

Early in August, in a clearing north of Winchell Lake, Anoki and Paji came upon an old pile of pulpwood and pine logs cut and abandoned by loggers long ago. The decayed logs and poles teemed with giant carpenter ants who had made nests in the rotten wood. The ants in turn attracted chipmunks and woodchucks, who fed upon them and burrowed among the rotten logs. Paji and Anoki ate hungrily as many ants as they could lick up, but they hoped to catch a nice fat woodchuck to make a really filling meal.

Anoki dug and scratched furiously at the dark openings among the logs where she could smell the woodchucks. A tiny shrew ran out, and she gobbled it up, but her angry growls and scrabbling produced no woodchuck. Meanwhile patient Paji waited, still and silent, on the other side of the log pile, and sure enough, before too long a plump, round woodchuck's head peered out. Clever Paji waited in ambush, not moving a muscle, till at last the woodchuck ventured forth, and Paji pounced. Her patient hunting methods had worked well, while Anoki's furious attack availed her naught.

When Anoki saw the fine fat woodchuck in Paji's jaws, she lost her temper altogether. Driven by hunger and frustration, she rushed at Paji in a fury and, taking poor Paji by surprise, seized the woodchuck and ran off. Anoki had often been cross and selfish in recent days, but never before had she treated Paji so unjustly. Even gentle Paji's patience had a limit, and now it had been reached. Her spirit was sore and hurt.

She decided she would take no more of Anoki's temper. While Anoki feasted greedily on Paji's woodchuck, Paji crept quietly away into the brush. She was still a far more timid young bear than her foster brother and sister, but she would rather travel through the woods alone than suffer Anoki's tantrums any longer. She headed north and east along a marshy stream and by nightfall had left Anoki far behind. In the warm August darkness she curled up to sleep beneath the Milky Way, and that night, for the first time since their birth, each of the cubs faced life in the wilderness entirely alone.

19. *Paji on Her Own*

All alone, Paji still wandered north and east along a small stream that soon turned into a chain of little unnamed lakes and rivers. The current flowed eastward, and on hot days she found it cool and peaceful to wade into the waters and float with the current wherever it chose to take her. This was all new country for Paji, with no familiar landmarks, but the lakes and streams, the pines and spruce bogs, were much like those she had lived among all her life.

She was still hungry much of the time, but now at least she could eat what food she found, since Anoki was not there to take it for herself. Yet she was lonely for the foster sister she had adored so long, and sometimes wished she hadn't run away from her. Hunting for mice and catching fish were easier when there were two bears to work together, and Paji had to spend long hours of patient hunting to catch even a few voles and shrews to ease her hunger. In the shallow pools she ran and splashed and rolled, chasing minnows in hopes they would wash up on sand and mud bars where she could catch them. To catch the bigger fish, Paji sat motionless on the bank, waiting, waiting for an unwary chub or sucker to stray within her reach.

Growing more lonesome every day, and with a constant hunger that never was quite satisfied, Paji followed the lake-and-river watercourse. She swam in the cool waters or waded in the shallows, pulling up coontails and lily roots when she could find them. When the current quickened and river rapids lay ahead, Paji at first would leave the stream and walk around the turbulent white water. But once by accident the swift current caught her by surprise and swept her over a small roaring waterfall.

Bobbing up in the pool below the falls, Paji found that this was the most fun she had had in days. It reminded her of the happy days last summer, rolling and tumbling down the Brule Lake hillside with Anoki and Anang. She was so buoyant and thick-furred that the rocks and boulders did not hurt her. Now she watched eagerly for each new fall and rapids in the stream and bounced and tumbled gaily over them like a large furry rubber ball.

Still trending eastward down the chain of waterways, she came to the north branch of the Arrowhead River and, soon after, to the Gunflint Trail. Here was the only traveled road into the northern wilderness, and here Paji paused, full of doubts and fears. She remembered well Kabato's warnings and the dangers of roads with their monster-trucks and the two-legged enemy, man. But the waterway flowed east, across the road, and Paji was too tired and hungry to turn back. A wild-rice bed lay just beyond the trail in a shallow marsh, and the hope of a rice banquet led Paji on.

For a long time she crouched in the brush by the roadside, alert and apprehensive. But no cars, no trucks, no men appeared along the Gunflint Trail. With a quick dash Paji crossed the road and soon was hidden once more deep among the rice stalks. Some of the rice was ripe, and she feasted on the nutty kernels, stripping the long stems with her mouth. But the crop was sparse and much of it still green, and Paji moved onward with her stomach far from full.

The next day she crossed Trap Lake, skirting the north shore and fishing along the way. She caught some minnows and a frog or two, but not enough to satisfy her hunger. In the warm late August afternoon she napped beneath a clump of spruces, and when night came she traveled on along the lake-shore. At the east end of Trap Lake a portage trail used by canoeists led through the woods to Crocodile Lake, which joined in turn the Crocodile River on a wilderness canoe route to the east.

The night was dark and moonless as Paji journeyed along the portage trail. Her broad paws made no sound on the soft forest floor, and her dark form blended with the nighttime shadows. Suddenly, without a scent or sound of warning, Paji rounded a bend in the trail and ran head-on into the one creature she most feared and dreaded—man! In the pitch darkness she tumbled backward, woofed in consternation, caught the fearful man-scent, and crashed away into the brush before the man, as startled as Paji, could catch his breath.

It was Art, the warden, who was traveling without a light, looking for poachers who had been illegally spearing and netting brook trout in the streams and rivers. He found no poachers on his midnight expedition, but he frightened and greatly troubled Paji. Long after the warden had gone on along the trail, she stayed hidden in the brush, afraid to move. The man-smell and the encounter in the darkness brought back Kabato's warnings still more strongly, and Paji knew that she should leave this area where man and his road intruded. When daylight came she would turn back, but for the rest of the night she slept in hiding under thick, brushy cover.

She slept late next morning and woke with a gnawing hunger. She must leave this dangerous territory, but also she must find food. Having turned back along the portage trail toward Trap Lake, she suddenly caught again the scent of man and, this time, the sound of voices. Swiftly and silently she hid beside the trail, watching as two men approached, one carrying a canoe upon his shoulders, the other laden down with tent, knapsack, and other camping gear.

A few rods past Paji's hiding place the second man set down his burdens on the trail and wiped his brow. "I'm bushed, Joe," he called to his companion. "I'll leave the food bag here and come back for it." And he picked up his other gear and plodded on along the portage after his companion. In a few moments all was quiet again along the trail, while there in the late August sunlight stood a big canvas bag that gave off odors to tempt any hungry animal. Even from a distance Paji's nose was set aquiver as smells of bacon and butter and dried milk and fruit mingled and drifted on the breeze toward her.

All her cautious instincts and all Kabato's wise and careful

training told her "No!"—but hunger urged her on. She crept out from the bushes and approached the tantalizing bag. Just at that moment she heard footsteps along the trail and dived once more into the underbrush. Back came the camper, just in time to save his food bag, and, unaware of Paji's presence, swung the canvas sack across his shoulder and marched back down the portage to Crocodile Lake.

The tantalizing smells of fruit and bacon had hypnotized poor Paji. Against her better judgment, fearful but oh, so hungry, she followed silently through the forest, keeping well out of sight. At the end of the portage, on Crocodile Lake, the two canoeists pitched their tent, hung up their food bag on a high tree limb, and paddled off for an afternoon of fishing.

All afternoon Paji circled the camp in hungry torment. The terrible man-smell was all about, and the man-creatures were still in sight out on the water; but high up on a pine tree hung the tempting food bag, well out of reach and dangling from a rope no bear could climb. Her wiser self urged Paji to go back, to leave this dangerous region; but still she prowled the forest, just out of sight, trying to think how she could reach the food.

At dusk the campers returned, built a campfire, and cooked their fish for supper, all unaware of the uninvited guest who watched them. The smells of frying fish made Paji hungrier than ever, while all she had for supper were a few grubs, ants, and balsam roots she dug in desperation. When darkness fell the campers yawned, doused the fire, and crawled into their tent. Soon all was still, and Paji felt that it was now or never.

Fearful and wary, she stole into the clearing. Stealthily she sniffed the campfire and all about the tent, hoping for crumbs or tidbits. But these were good campers who buried their garbage deep and kept their campsite clean, so there was nothing for Paji save that high-hanging food bag. Gathering her courage, she climbed the pine tree and crept out along the limb toward the dangling bag. Farther, farther out she inched and almost reached it—when, crash! the pine branch broke, the bag fell down, and Paji landed with a thud not three feet from the campers' tent.

Pandemonium broke out. From the tent there came the loudest and most terrifying sounds poor Paji had ever heard, a banging and a clanging that split her eardrums and sent her heart into her mouth. Without a thought for fruit or bacon, she took off as fast as she could go, running for dear life back toward Trap Lake, back to deep woods, back where there were no roads or men or terrifying noises, where bears could live in peace and quiet, no matter how slim their rations.

Paji was lucky, for the campers she had met were wise in the ways of the woods. They knew they must hang their food high to protect it, and they knew how to frighten away a hungry bear with no harm to either the bear or themselves. They merely banged their cooking pots together, a far better and safer way to guard a campsite than any gun. Sleepily the campers rehung their food bag and, chuckling about the bear story they could tell back home, crawled back into the tent and went to sleep.

20. Anoki Learns a Lesson

When Paji left Anoki at the woodpile, Anoki was too busy and too cross to notice her departure. She had eaten up Paji's woodchuck in short order and returned to the pile of decayed logs to look for more. She knew that there were several still hiding among the timbers, for she could hear them whistling derisively at her efforts to dig them out. Anoki scratched and clawed in fury, still hungry, and angry at being thwarted. She growled and called impatiently for Paji to come and help her, but Paji did not come.

Suddenly one key log moved under Anoki's furious efforts, and in a flash log after massive log rolled down from the great pile. In the nick of time Anoki dodged out of the way before they rolled over her. But the woodchucks were not so lucky.

Three had been killed by the rolling logs, and now Anoki had a feast indeed. She ate another woodchuck as fast as she could gobble, and then, with hunger satisfied for the first time in many days, she called repentantly to Paji to offer her a woodchuck in atonement.

Paji did not answer, and when Anoki looked for her she could not find her. Her scent led to the nearby stream and then was lost, and Anoki could not tell which way she had traveled. Anoki was sorry now that she had been so selfish, and suddenly the woods seemed lonely without her foster sister. But she could keep the woodchucks for herself, she thought, and carefully she scratched dry leaves and grass over them to hide them for tomorrow's breakfast.

She slept that night in a nearby clump of sumac. Early next morning, just after dawn, she was awakened by a brushy rustle and leaping up, she saw two timber wolves run off, each with a woodchuck in its mouth. Snarling with rage, Anoki chased them, wishing again that Paji were there to help her; but the wolves soon outdistanced her, and poor Anoki was left without her breakfast.

Was this the same crafty wolf pair that had tried to steal Kabato's deer carcass last spring? No one could say, but the memory of Kabato and those happy family days made Anoki still more sad and lonely. No one came now to help her guard her food supply—not kind Kabato whom she had disobeyed, nor Koda, the friendly stranger, nor Anang, her playful brother, not even Paji, whom she now missed most of all.

Anoki traveled northward, following no course or plan but

moving wherever she found food in this lean summer season. Here and there a few blueberries, already old and dried, clung to the bushes; but the late spring frost had left its mark on nearly every berry patch. Spruce tops and old skunk cabbages, dry cinnamon ferns and ants helped keep her going. But it takes a lot of ants to fill a bear, and Anoki was never really filled. Now and then she found a yellowjackets' nest in the ground and dug and ate them, stings and all. When she found ruffed grouse feeding on bearberries, she tried to catch the grouse. But they were far too quick for her and flew away, leaving Anoki with a few bearberries to finish up.

Anoki's wanderings brought her late in August to the Gunflint Trail, not many miles from where Paji had crossed it. Like Paji, she hesitated long at this warning sign of man, for she too remembered the wardens on the logging trail who had tried to carry her away. From deep among the pines she watched and listened as several cars went by, for this was a busy weekend near the end of the tourist season. Man and his cars alarmed her, but not too far away she caught the scent of food—decaying food, and the smell was luscious to Anoki.

Following her nose, Anoki found a clearing in the woods where one of the resorts along the trail had made a garbage dump. All summer long the garbage from the guest cabins was hauled here, and ravens and foxes and many other creatures were tempted to come and scavenge. In this lean summer black bears especially were drawn by hunger to the garbage dump, and tourists came to watch them scratch among the tin cans and melon rinds for food the woods did not provide so easily this year. Many tourists who knew no better brought bread and sweets to feed the hungry bears, and the foolish resort owner was pleased to have the bears as an attraction for his paying guests.

At dusk Anoki watched from the shadows while a big mother black bear and two first-year cubs drank Coca-Cola from bottles held by a group of tourists. Anoki was consumed by hunger, but even so she could not forget Kabato's teachings. She was alarmed to see black bears so close to their two-legged enemies, and though the scent of food was tantalizing, she did not approach the dump until the tourists left.

For over a week Anoki stayed in the region, sleeping by day deep in the woods and feeding at night at the garbage dump. She was troubled and uneasy, for she knew that she was disobeying Kabato's teachings. This was man-territory, and danger lay all about; but she was hungry, and the food enticed her. Night after night she gorged on stale bread, rotten oranges, fish cleanings, and all the other residue of many tourist cabins. Unlike the other bears, she never showed herself when tourists came to watch, but slowly her dependence on man's cast-off food began to grow.

Early in September, without warning, the garbage dumping stopped. Night after night the bears picked over the same old cans and paper wrappers, finding no nourishment and nothing new to eat. They could not know that Labor Day had come and gone, ending the tourist season. All the paying guests had gone back to the cities, and now the resort owner closed his

cabins for the winter. He gave no thought to the hungry bears whom he had lured all summer and who now had grown dependent on man's garbage.

Anoki and the other bears grew hungrier each day. This was the time when bears should eat most heavily to fatten for the winter, but the poor bears who had become garbage addicts no longer knew how to find food for themselves. One night Anoki smelled fish frying, a smell so delicious that she could not help seeking it out. The mother bear and her two cubs had smelled it too, and silently they all prowled toward the resort kitchen, where the tantalizing odor floated out the open back door.

Anoki's caution kept her from approaching closely, and she lurked in the darkness, torn between alarm and hunger. But the mother bear was desperate. Her own hunger and her hungry cubs impelled her onward, and she walked boldly up onto the porch and scratched imploringly at the open door. A scream rang out, the sound of running feet, and then, "Crack, crack"—two rifle shots and then two more. The mother bear whirled, staggered, and fell dead, while in the darkness two small cubs cowered and whined in terror.

A cruel, needless end had come to one black bear, a bear who meant no harm to anyone but who had been corrupted by man's enticements. The resort owner did not know or care about county laws forbidding the killing of black bears, for he thought his home endangered and the bears a nuisance now that the tourist season was over. Next day he called the wardens to remove the bear cubs; and this time, with heavy hearts to see such useless slaughter, Art and Charlie did carry off the orphaned cubs to raise in happier surroundings.

Anoki heard the shots from deep within the shadows, but, even though she was way across the clearing, one bullet grazed her shoulder. Running in terror through the darkness, she thought only of escape, of leaving this evil region and man's cruel temptations. All night she traveled in desperate haste, back along the route that she had come, far from the Gunflint Trail, the garbage dump, and all signs and sounds of man. Her shoulder hurt her, but the pain was nothing to the fear and shock she felt at the sad scene she had witnessed and her own narrow escape. Hunger and natural enemies she could endure, but never again would she forget Kabato's lessons about the treachery of man.

Retracing her steps southwest toward Winchell Lake, Anoki was tired and lonely as well as hungry. She had grown far wiser and more mature as a result of her experiences, and never again would she be the foolish, selfish cub of recent months. As days grew cooler and September passed she fished and hunted earnestly, with far more patience than she used to have, and scoured each bush and log for berries, worms, or grubs.

One mid-fall day Anoki came again into the clearing where the old woodpile was, where she and Paji last had hunted together. There was the fallen woodpile, with logs widely scattered. Anoki scouted carefully around the rotten logs, seeking a few remaining ants or mice, when from the brush beside the nearby stream she heard a splashing and a bearlike grunt.

Anoki sniffed the breeze. Could it be? Oh, could it really

be—and then she bounded through the bushes to the stream bank. Yes, it was Paji, gentle, patient Paji, making her own slow way back up the lakes and streams to the deep wilderness she too had strayed from. Anoki stood hesitantly by the bank, not sure if Paji would welcome her. But Paji was older and wiser too, and past grievances were forgotten. With a soft, happy grunt she greeted her foster sister and offered her one of the brook trout she had caught. Grateful and glad, Anoki ate the fish while Paji caressed her sister tenderly and licked her healing wound.

Together again, Anoki and Paji with one accord moved southward toward the deep wilderness they had known as cubs, far from the paths of man. Each of them had learned a lesson she never would forget, the lesson Kabato had always tried to teach them. Never again would they be tempted by man's foods and blandishments, but would shun his roads and campgrounds, cabins and resorts, and live wild and free deep in the woods, where black bears belong.

And it seemed that Nature at last took pity on the hunger that the bears had felt all summer. Now in September the brook trout were spawning in the streams, acorns had ripened on the scrub oaks, and cranberries, too hardy for the frosts to kill, hung red and ripe at last in many bogs. Thorn apples provided an occasional treat when trout and other fish grew tiresome.

All through the fall Paji and Anoki fed and fattened, moving slowly southward toward their old familiar haunts. Late in October, in an early snowstorm, they came into the cedar swamp where Anoki and Anang had been born. Both bears were sleepy now and ready to find winter shelter. Anoki's goal was once again the big pine on the ridge, but Paji was too sleepy to hold out. While snowflakes swirled around them, Paji found the old fallen cedar in the swamp, crawled into the den beneath its roots, and drifted off into her winter slumber.

Anoki plodded on, drowsy but still determined to reach the hollow pine. Climbing the ridge, she followed the worn trail she knew so well. At the pine's entrance she stopped, surprised, for deep within she heard the rhythmic breathing of another sleeping bear. Sniffing with growing joy, Anoki crawled halfway into the entrance, and there, sound asleep, was Kabato, her dear, big mother, whom she had missed so often. For a long happy moment she watched Kabato deep in sleep; then she withdrew and turned north up the trail.

Kabato needed that safe, big den especially, for she would have new cubs to nurse and tend this winter, and somehow Anoki knew this was the way it should be. Sleepily she traveled on to find another den. She knew where to go—the rocky cave near where the otters played, and where they all had slept on previous journeys. Two ridges over and north a little way— there was the den beneath the bank, just as Anoki remembered it. Tired and sleepy, but a wiser bear than she had ever been, Anoki settled in for her third winter.

21. Anang Meets Danger

All summer while Paji and Anoki traveled together, quarreled,
and parted, Anang had made his way alone. In July, when he
set out to follow Koda and Kabato, their trail was already
many hours old. Their scents were faint or blown away entirely, and gradually Anang grew more and more discouraged.
He yearned to find his idolized father and travel with him as
a friend and equal, and if Kabato cared to tag along, Anang
wouldn't mind, if she would stop her cuffs and scoldings.

But Koda and Kabato had other plans. They covered their
trail well so none of the cubs could follow, and traveled fast
and free into new regions where they could be undisturbed.
In more than a week of searching Anang could find no trace

of either parent, and he reluctantly gave up, at least for now, his dream of comradeship with Koda.

Slowly he worked his way back to the little lake where he had last seen Paji and Anoki. But they too were gone, he knew not where, and with a lonely heart he wandered disconsolately back to the old pine ridge. The scarcity of berries kept him on the edge of hunger, but he ate balsam boughs and roots and clover, and frogs and garter snakes when he could find them. Like Koda, he had come to be an expert fisherman, and when all else failed he could usually catch a sucker for his dinner. In the hot days of summer and in the warmer waters, the suckers did not taste as good as they did in the spring and fall. But in this lean year for black bears Anang was glad for any fish he could catch.

At the end of the pine ridge, on the steep banks above the Cascade River, Anang searched along the rocky ledge where last spring he had frolicked so gaily with his father and his sisters. There was the den beneath the overhang where the cubs had slept; there was the rushing river, lower and quieter now but still flowing southward down the hills and ridges to Lake Superior. But there was no sign of any bears, no trace of any of his family; and sadly, without a conscious plan or purpose, Anang began to travel down the Cascade River.

He kept well back among the pines and aspens, lest any enemies should be about in this new region. But though a dirt road paralleled the river for some distance on the other side, he saw and heard no signs of man. On hot August days he stayed deep within the forest, sleeping in cool, dark thickets, and came out only at night to fish along the banks and wade or swim in the cool waters. One day he found the first blueberries he had seen all summer, a large, lush patch that had escaped the frost because of mist and fog along the river. Here he stayed for several days, eating his fill till every berry was consumed.

Farther on he found the first warning sign of man—an old abandoned lumber camp. The buildings were decayed and tumbling down, and here Anang found bugs, ants, and mice aplenty among the rotted logs and timbers. He swatted the scurrying mice with his broad paws as if they were flies, then tossed them into his mouth and ate them as you and I eat peanuts. Anang felt safe in this deserted camp, for it was many years since man had used it, but it was a warning that he should have heeded. If man had been here once, he might be nearby also, and Anang was to learn that lesson in a very painful way.

Leaving the lumber camp and following along the river's course, he now found far slimmer pickings. The land was sparse and brushy in many places, and there were no fruits or berries, no rotten logs or anthills to nourish a hungry growing bear. There were few fish in the river here, no rice beds and no lily roots. Anang grew hungrier as each day passed, but always he hoped that the next hillside, the next bend in the river, would bring him to a land of plenty such as he had known last summer at Brule Lake.

In one grove of trees he found a big black birch stub buzzing and humming with a giant hive of bees. He smelled the honey deep within, and frantically he clawed and tore at the hive entrance to enlarge it. But the hole was small and quite far up the trunk, and Anang had trouble clinging to the trunk and clawing at the same time. The bees stung him savagely, and the birch wood was firm and did not yield easily. Poor Anang clawed till his paws were bleeding, but still could not get at the honey.

Hungry and disappointed, he gave up. He waded in the river to drown the bees that still clung to his fur, and eased their stings in the cool water. Then once again he traveled on, still hungry, lonesome, and drawing ever closer to unsuspected danger.

Several miles northeast of Grand Marais, east of the Cascade River and north of Lake Superior's shore, Anang came out of a cut-over woodland tract into a wide clearing. Between the woods and the clearing there ran a strange structure such as he had never seen. It was a fence, and the clearing was a pasture. Anang had come to one of the few small northern farms that lie scattered through Cook County a few miles back from Lake Superior.

The strange appearance of the fence should have warned him that this was part of man's civilization and none of Anang's affair. But curiosity led him to follow the fence a little way along the woods. A quarter-mile from the river the fence stopped at a rolling oatfield. There in the early September sunlight Anang saw rod after rod of golden, ripening grain, the full, juicy kernels nodding on the two-foot oat stalks, not quite ready to be harvested by man but just right for a hungry bear who needed to fatten for the winter. The twenty-acre field looked like a sea of plenty to Anang, and he could hardly wait for darkness to begin his feast.

His caution kept him hiding in the woods until darkness had fallen, but it did not occur to him that these were man's oats, in man's territory, and that a wise bear would leave at once, hungry or not, and return to bear territory. Instead he waited eagerly for nightfall, and when a great round harvest moon rose above the hills he crept out from the brush and began his banquet. He swept up pawfuls of the golden stalks and stripped the grain into his mouth, eating his way slowly across one corner of the field. His big paws and bulky body trampled and spoiled as much grain as he ate, but he was happy and careless as he harvested, for there was plenty more.

Anang ate oats until he nearly burst, then went back to the river to slake his thirst. Barely able to waddle, he crawled into a thick tangle of vines and brambles in the woods and went to sleep, peaceful and satisfied. The next night and the next he

returned to the oatfield to gorge and fatten on the nourishing grain. Each night he went to a different part of the field, and on the third night, from a rise in the rolling oatfield, he noticed for the first time lights and buildings in the distance. Now his better judgment told him, with no ifs or buts, that he should leave at once; but the wide field of oats still unharvested tempted him beyond resistance. Just one more night of luscious feeding, Anang thought, and he slept another day deep in his bramble tangle.

On the fourth day, while Anang was fast asleep, the farmer came to see how his oats were ripening. When he saw the trampled swaths and grain-stripped stalks he knew at once a bear had done the damage. Angrily he called his sons to bring their hunting dogs and vowed tonight they would catch that bear and kill him.

"You can't kill him, Pa," one of the boys told him. "Cook County has a law you can't kill bear except in deer-hunting season." The boy was right. Cook County passed that law to protect bears as a tourist attraction, while all the rest of Minnesota has open season on the black bear all year round, and men may kill as many as they please. How right the black bears are to fear and shun mankind and all his cruel ways, for the only reason man does not exterminate the bears is to exploit them as a lure for tourist money!

"Call the warden," the farmer said in anger. "No bear is going to spoil my oats and get away with it."

When Art the warden heard the story he also told the farmer he could not shoot the bear. "Fire over his head if you see him," Art instructed, "and he'll run off and not bother your fields again."

Grumbling and in bad temper, the farmer waited for full darkness. Then, with his pack of dogs running ahead, he and his sons approached the oatfield with their guns and flashlights. Tonight Anang had ventured to the edge of the field farthest from the woods. He was feeding greedily on the delicious grain when suddenly the dogs came running, yapping and barking as they caught his scent.

If this had been a pack of wolves threatening his rightful interests, Anang would have stood his ground and fought them to the finish. But he heard men's voices calling, shots rang out, and bullets whizzed above his head. He ran for the woods as fast as he could go; but he was fat and sluggish from his feasting, and in a moment the dogs were at his heels. Instinctively and without thinking, Anang dashed for a tall spruce at the edge of the woods and climbed to the upper boughs.

Now he was treed, with no way to escape. An older and wiser bear would have run for the river, where he could swim better than the dogs and drown those who dared to follow. But poor Anang was now surrounded and at the mercy of both dogs and men with guns. With all his heart he wished that he had heeded his mother's teachings, or that Kabato or Koda could come to help him. Never had he felt so alone and frightened.

The dogs set up a steady yapping all around the tree, and men and boys gathered on the ground below Anang. The gunshots and commotion had waked the neighbors, and lights went

on at nearby farms and people walked across the fields to find out what was going on. Bright flashlights shone in Anang's face, and loud, excited talk disturbed the night.

"I'm going to shoot and eat him," the farmer shouted, but the neighbors calmed him down. "Wait till morning and call the warden," they advised him; and though he cursed and muttered, the angry farmer did as they advised. All night the dogs and boys stood guard to prevent Anang's escape, and in the morning Art the warden drove out to see what all the fuss was about.

"Why, that bear's just a scared half-grown cub," Art said as he looked up at Anang, now more frightened and confused than ever after the long night in the tree. "He's learned his lesson. Call off your dogs, and all you folks go home, and that bear will come down and go back in the woods where he belongs. Just let him go, and I'm certain he won't bother you again."

Still grumbling, the farmer did as Art said. When all the dogs and people had disappeared, Art watched through his binoculars as poor Anang at last dared to clamber down the tree and run for the woods, the river, and the wilderness. As Art watched him go, it seemed to him he'd seen that young black bear before. "I must be dreaming," he chuckled to himself, and neither he nor Anang would ever know that Art, who once had nearly stolen Anang from his mother, had righted that wrong by saving Anang's life.

22. Koda to the Rescue

Anang ran through the woods till he could run no more. Even then he kept a fast and anxious pace as he moved north along the river, returning the way he'd come. His only thought was to go back once more to the deep, quiet forests where he had grown up, safe from men and dogs and guns, where a bear could live in happiness and peace.

Better to be hungry and free than fatten on man's food or fields; this was the lesson that Anang had learned, just as Paji and Anoki in recent weeks had learned it too. Each cub in a different way had found out for himself that hunger is a less deadly enemy than man, and never again, in all their adult lives, would they be tempted to leave the wilderness.

But even now Anang had not escaped all danger. Traveling

as fast as he could move, he had put several miles behind him by nightfall; but when night came, he still pushed on in spite of darkness. Padding in haste along an unfamiliar trail, he crossed a log and stepped into a wolf trap set by another farmer to catch stray wolf marauders. As the trap snapped he leaped aside, but one forepaw was firmly caught. In pain and terror Anang pulled and tugged to get his foot loose, but the trap held fast, both to his foot and to a stub of the log to which it was chained. In spite of the pain he went on pulling with all his strength to gain his freedom, and with a sudden crack the stub gave way. Head over heels Anang fell backward, freed from the log but with the trap, chain, and wood stub still dangling from his throbbing paw.

With his teeth and one good forepaw he tore desperately at the steel-jawed trap till both front paws were bleeding, but he could not release the heavy spring. In panic he tried to hobble along the trail, but the dangling chain and stub caught in the brush, and the pain became still greater than before. Blindly he stumbled down the river bank into the water, and there the coolness soothed his poor trapped paw a little. As the pain eased slightly, he drowsed and nodded in the water, for it was nearly two days since he had slept. At last, in utter exhaustion, he crawled out of the water and found a bed of pine needles beneath low-hanging boughs along the bank. Whining and moaning softly, he fell into a feverish and fitful slumber.

He dozed through the chill September night, waking and dreaming alternately. He dreamed he was helping Kabato and his sisters gather honey, and swarms of bees kept stinging his poor paw. In the early dawn he thought he heard a soft "Woof, woof," and, looking up, he saw a giant bear beside him. He thought he was still dreaming feverish dreams, his old fond dream of finding Koda and roaming the forests with him. Whimpering, he closed his eyes to dream again, when suddenly he felt a gentle nudge. His eyes flew open, he sat up groggily, and as he felt his paw throb dully, he knew this was no dream. It was really Koda, his own father, who loomed above him on the river bank.

But Anang was in such pain he could hardly realize that his dream of finding Koda had come true. His paw had swollen further overnight, and now the trap was sunk deep in the flesh. When Koda called him to follow, Anang could not even crawl, and Koda came back to see what was the matter. He seemed

to know at once what the trouble was and what to do. Crouching beside Anang, he took the sprung jaws of the trap between his teeth, and with his own strong jaws he slowly pressed the steel trap open. Slowly the spring let go, and at the crucial moment he pulled the trap free from Anang's forepaw.

In the first moments when the trap was off, the pain seemed worse than ever as the blood returned and every nerve cried out. But soon Anang felt better and for the first time could savor the joy of Koda's presence.

Now Koda grunted to him again and led the way upriver to a muddy spring. Anang limped after him as best he could and followed him into the cool deep muck. While Koda rolled and wallowed, Anang's paw slowly ceased its throbbing in the soothing poultice of the mud. The relief from pain was so relaxing that, with his head pillowed on the bank, tired Anang went off to sleep right in the mud bath.

Hours later, when Anang awoke, Koda had disappeared. It was late afternoon, and the fall air was growing chill. Anang's paw felt much better, well enough to limp along on, but he was sad and anxious lest he had lost Koda once again. Sniffing about the spring, he found a mud trail through the brush along the river, where every bush and clump of grass was covered with a coat of mud. Yes, Koda must have passed this way after his mud bath, and now Anang hobbled along in fond pursuit.

Not far up the river Anang came to a clearing, and there stood Koda in a grove of thorn apples, stripping the red haws and feeding on them. The pulpy fruit looked good to Anang, for though he had gorged on oats, it was several days now since he had eaten. Hesitant but hopeful, he waited at the edge of the clearing. Would Koda let him join him, or was he ready to move on alone, now that Anang was well? The mating season was long past, and Koda and Kabato had parted once again, but still, it was not every black bear father who would welcome a young bear's company.

With anxious heart Anang waited for Koda to make a sign. Slowly Koda rose to his full height, broke off a branch of red thorn apples, and with a soft grunt invited Anang to come and eat. Brimming with happiness, Anang limped out to join Koda, and side by side the two black bears, big cub and bigger father, fed peacefully in the September twilight.

Day after day, through rainy late September and a bright, brisk October, Koda and Anang traveled together back to the deep woods and silent lakes. Koda had followed the Cascade River southward to feed on the thorn apples that had escaped the frosts; but when those fruits were gone they traveled steadily northward.

One day they passed the black birch bee tree where Anang had tried so hard to get the honey. He could not resist the challenge once again, and even with his wounded paw he clawed and scratched in hopes of tasting honey. At last Koda, with an impatient grunt, told Anang to stand aside, and with his mighty jaws and paws he bit and tore the firm wood from the entrance. Now he could reach in his arm to steal the honeycomb, and while the bees buzzed and stung, each bear in turn scooped out great gobs of honey.

It was a feast to remember, for the tree held nearly a hundred pounds of honeycomb, and honey was just the dessert Anang and Koda craved for their fall fattening. Anang had had his fill of oats—his first and last experience with that food —and he was well padded for the winter. He weighed more than two hundred pounds now and showed every sign of growing eventually almost to Koda's size. So both big bears ate heartily and seldom passed up an opportunity to hunt for food or fish.

The long, lean summer was over now and Anang's torn paw was healed. Acorns, nannyberries, and thorn apples eked out this year's scarce supply of berries; but next year the berries should be plentiful again, with plums and cherries lush for all to feed upon. Meanwhile Anang and Koda stopped at every rotten log and stump and tore it apart to look for grubs and insects, and many a mouse and garter snake met sudden doom when these two bears passed by.

As October ended, Anang and Koda grew less interested in food. Padded with fat and covered with thick glossy fur, the bears were nearly ready for the long cold winter. The trees were bare, and ice had formed in the shallow pools along the Cascade River as Koda and Anang approached once more the bluff where the pine ridge ended, where Koda had first met his family.

Koda sniffed carefully along the whole rock ledge, remembering perhaps that happy meeting and wondering where all his family had wandered. But Anang was sleepy, too sleepy now even to follow Koda, and with a happy sigh he crawled into the den below the cliff and settled into a peaceful winter slumber.

The next day snow began to fall upon the forests, a light and silent snowfall that clung to branches and hushed the calls of owls and chickadees. The silent fall of snow made Koda drowsy, and soon he too was ready to find a winter den. Remembering the fallen cedar in the swamp, he made his way along the deer trails toward it. But when he peered into the deep and cozy hollow, there was Paji, his foster cub, deep in her winter sleep.

Silently Koda moved on. Up the pine ridge and along the trail, he stopped again at the old hollow pine where all his family had slept the previous winter. Even before he crawled into the entrance he scented that Kabato had chosen this den once more, in preparation for their new cubs that would be born this winter. Proud and happy that his mate was near, Koda traveled on along the ridge, searching in growing drowsiness for a place to spend the winter. Not far away he knew another den beneath the rocks, and sleepily, yawning and blinking, he plodded to it. There was Anoki, snug beneath the rocky ledge and sound asleep, dreaming long dreams of summer days and frolics.

Koda went on, but all the world seemed blurred and hazy to his sleepy brain. The snowflakes swirled around him, sighing softly in the pine boughs, and now big, drowsy Koda could go no farther. Half asleep, he scratched a nest in a soft hollow amid a clump of spruces, and he curled his big body beneath the low-hanging branches. Slowly the soft snow sifted down through the branches, covering him with a thick white blanket. Soon, as the flakes fell deep and fast, no one could tell where a giant black bear slept beneath the snow.

Koda's last thoughts before he fell asleep were of his mate and cubs, all safe and settled for the winter, deep in the sheltering forest. Next spring they all would part once more, with each cub ready soon to find a mate and start a new family of its own. They would live out their independent lives, each traveling on his own; but in the forests and on the hillsides, at streams and berry patches, they all would meet again from time to time. Deep in the northern wilderness, far from the haunts of man, they would live always as black bears should, wild and free, at peace with God and Nature and with their north-woods neighbors.